The Puzzle

OF

Ancient Man

Donald E. Chittick, Ph.D.

CREATION COMPASS

THE PUZZLE OF ANCIENT MAN
Second Edition © 1998 by Donald E. Chittick

Printed in the United States of America

Published by Creation Compass
P. O. Box 993
Newberg, Oregon 97132-0993

ISBN 0-9640978-1-8

To my wife Donna

for her prayers, help,
and encouragement

Acknowledgments

This book is an outgrowth of suggestions from many who have heard my lectures on ancient man. Their many helpful comments and suggestions are appreciated. It was largely their urging and encouragement which moved me to write. I wish to express especially my gratitude to the following:

Editorial Contributions:
Donna Chittick
Ron & Shelly Chapin
Ken Ham
Craig & Annie Major
John Morris
Don & Alice Watt

Research Resources:
Dennis Swift

Layout & Production:
Craig & Annie Major
Diane King
Brandon R. Vallorani

Cover Design:
Mark Bain
Brandon R. Vallorani

Photographs:
Steven and Carla Allemann
Philip Burgi
Helen Culp
Mrs. DeMille
David Hooley
Seth Wilson
Lloyd Wright Jr. (digitizing)

Typing:
Donna Chittick

TABLE OF CONTENTS

INTRODUCTION

There are two widely held views about where mankind originated. One is that we have been directly created in the image of God our Creator, just as Genesis chapter one tells us. The other view is that man has evolved up from the animal by a long series of evolutionary changes. If the second view were true, then it logically follows that the further we went into the past, the more primitive ought man to be. In other words, if we had come up from the animal, then as we move further and further into the past, human artifacts should be more and more "primitive". However, what do the findings of science show us? They seem to indicate exactly the opposite. With the possible exception of the amazing developments of the past one hundred years, the further we go into the past, the higher was the level of science and technology as reflected by human artifacts. Why, if man ascended up from the animal, do human artifacts not reflect this gradual improvement? How do we explain the fact that ancient human artifacts such as what appear to be batteries and sophisticated mechanical computing devices, and other items, seem to show that man possessed a high level of technology even in the distant past? What explanation will make sense of the available evidence? This riddle needs to be solved and is the reason for our title, the puzzle of ancient man.

In Part One of this book we will focus on the puzzle of ancient man as it relates to the conflict between high-quality ancient human artifacts and the assumed evolution of man. Several lines of evidence will be examined such as that from human artifacts and historical records, including the Bible. Part Two of the book will cover philosophical issues, the relationship of the Bible and science, and some fossil and biochemical evidence.

Following are some of the questions we will address. "Does fossil evidence show that man evolved upward from the animals?" "What is the explanation for Neanderthal and other so-called Cave Man fossils?" "What about 'race'?" "Where and how did the various 'races' originate?" "How do the Egyptian pyramids or the unique drawings in the Nazca Desert of South America fit in?"

In order for us to achieve a total picture of man's ancestry, all of this evidence (human artifacts, fossils, and historical records) must be taken into account. For an accurate picture of man's past, no evidence must be censored, purposely omitted, or ignored. When all of these areas of evidence are considered, a picture emerges which not only provides satisfying answers to the questions such as those above, but also one which lends support to the total accuracy of the Scriptural account of man's origin.

In Part One, our approach to this study will be as follows. First we will provide an overview of man's origin and early history as given in the Bible. Next, representative samples of actual evidence will be examined and compared with the competing worldviews. Then in the final section it will be shown how the Bible best matches with reality and provides a basis for putting the puzzle pieces together.

Part Two of the book considers two important aspects of the puzzle of ancient man. Chapter 14 concerns the relationship of the Bible and science, what constitutes a scientific explanation, and the place of logic and evidence. Chapter 15 focuses on some fossil and biochemical evidence. In order to have a solid understanding of issues relating to ancient man, one needs to consider the logical and philosophical foundations as well. My first inclination was to begin the book with a discussion of these foundations. However, not everyone may find these items to be of immediate interest. Therefore some who reviewed the original manuscript recommended to either omit the discussion entirely, or to add it as a separate part. I have chosen the latter course. When traced to its root cause, the puzzle of ancient man can be seen to arise from conflicting worldviews about the origin and nature of man. In other words, the issue stems from conflicting faiths or philosophical systems. As already mentioned above, in one system man originated as a direct act of creation and in the other man evolved up from an animal. These two belief systems are antithetical. They cannot both be true at the same time. Both cannot reflect reality.

Current culture challenges the idea that man has been created. Particularly it challenges the Biblical concept of man's creation. Thus it is commonly stated or implied that the Biblical account of origins does not represent an actual historical account. It does not represent reality. However, in contrast to much popular belief, as we shall see, the Bible <u>does</u> accurately portray man's origin and history. It does reflect reality.

One further note may aid the reader in capturing the meaning of certain passages throughout the book. As an aid to my writing, I have chosen to follow the rules for good English grammar and other suggestions provided by the reference manual Rod and Staff English Handbook (Rod and Staff Publishers, Inc., Crockett, Kentucky 41413 [1983]). These rules follow the historical and traditional usage and grammar rules of the English language.

PART ONE

OUT OF PLACE ARTIFACTS

There is no convincing evidence for man's evolution. For a summary of the lack of evidence required to support man's evolution, please consult Chapter 15. In addition to the negative fossil evidence and negative biochemical evidence for human evolution, evolutionism must face up to yet another disturbing problem with evidence, that of human artifacts. Human beings leave behind evidence of their presence and activities. Artifacts from the past can be used to provide much information about ancient man and his activities. However such artifacts pose a very great problem for the evolutionary picture that man developed upward from the animals. If evolution is correct, and man came up from the animal, then the further into the past one goes, the more primitive ought man to be. Artifacts should be increasingly primitive as we move further into the past. The actual case with the evidence, however, seems to be just the opposite.

In fact the cultural remains of ancient man are so at odds with the evolutionary picture for man's origin that a special term has been coined to describe these artifacts. The term is OOPArts, an acronym for Out Of Place Artifacts. What are some examples? Rock hounds collecting geodes in the Cosa Mountains of California discovered what appeared to be an electrical device of vast antiquity.

> Sliced in two, the object showed a hexagonal part, a porcelain or ceramic insulator with a central metallic shaft, and the remains of a corroded piece of metal with threads. The overall impression is that the object in the geode is man-made and not a bizarre trick of nature. It appears to be some kind of electrical device - specifically, a spark plug.[1]

A spark plug is evidence of fairly sophisticated development. Reliable dates for such finds are difficult to obtain. However, it has been commonly assumed that formation of geodes requires significant amounts of time. Finding a spark plug in a rock considered to be very old would indeed give it the label of an out-of-place artifact. Evidence of advanced technology, like spark plugs, should not, according to evolutionism, be discovered in old rocks. Even more surprising perhaps is the discovery of an object located on a ship that was sunk in the Aegean Sea before the time of Christ.[2] It appeared to be some type of mechanical computing device. Modern computers are of two types: analog and digital. The object discovered on this ship sunk before Christ's time was a fairly sophisticated analog computer. It apparently was used for navigation purposes aboard ships and for aiding in making accurate maps.

Contrary to much modern teaching, it is now known that navigation as an exact science had already been well

---

[1] Brad Steiger, "Were Ancient Scientists Really Tuned to Today?" *Parade*, March 4, 1979, p. 10

[2] "The Seminal Science" *Mosaic* May/June 1978, pp. 2-8

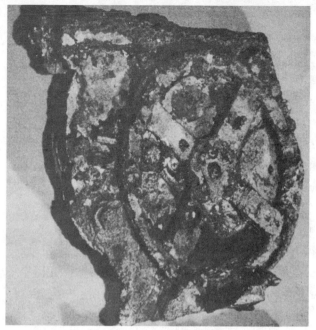

An analog computing device or "computer" was recovered from a ship which had sunk in the Aegean Sea in the first century B.C. The device incorporated very sophisticated gears, even differential gears, a type not re-discovered until modern times.

Photos courtesy of the National Science Foundation

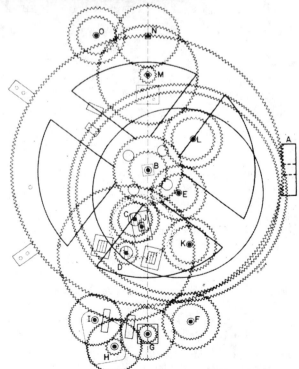

developed even in remote antiquity. One line of evidence pointing to this conclusion is the existence of copies of ancient maps. Some of these maps show features of the earth's surface that we can only see by using modern instrumentation.[3]

At first, one might be tempted to think that these and other "out-of-place" artifacts are just a few oddities. However, many such artifacts are known and are documented in various sources.[4] Material in these references shows that OOPArts are not an anomaly.

Instead they attest to a high and technologically advanced civilization in the distant past. In fact from a consideration of such evidence, we might even wonder along with one well-known scientist, Thor Heyerdahl, "whether civilization did indeed peak long, long ago."[5]

These and other evidences will be discussed in greater detail in later chapters. For now we simply want to illustrate

[3]Charles Hapgood, *Maps of the Ancient Sea Kings: Evidence of Advanced Civilization in the Ice Age*, Philadelphia, Chilton Books, 1966

[4]Charles Berlitz, *Mysteries From Forgotten Worlds,* Garden City NY, Doubleday & Co. 1972;

William R. Corliss, *Ancient Man: A Handbook of Puzzling Artifacts*, Glen Arm MD, The Sourcebook Project, 1978;

Rene Noorbergen, *Secrets of the Lost Races: New Discoveries of Advanced Technology in Ancient Civilizations*, Collegedale TN, Norcom Publishing Corp., 1992;

Charles Michael Boland, *They all discovered America*, New York, Permabook, 1963;

Barry Fell, America B.C.: *Ancient Settlers in the New World*, New York, Quadrangle/The New York Times Book Co., 1977 (also by Barry Fell, *Bronze Age America*);

O. Neugebauer, *The Exact Sciences in Antiquity*, New York, Dover Publications, 1969;

Graham Hancock, *Fingerprints of the Gods*, New York, Crown Trade Paperbacks, 1995;

Michael A. Cremo and Richard L. Thompson, *Forbidden Archeology*, San Diego, Govardhan Hill Publishing, 1993

[5]Thomas Moore, "Thor Heyerdahl: Sailing Against the Current" *U.S. News & World Report*, April 2, 1990, p. 60

the point that reality (OOPArts in this case) does not fit with the naturalistic paradigm. (A paradigm is a belief system for explaining evidence. See p. 140)

As remains of ancient cultures around the world are examined and carefully studied, a recurring theme or pattern emerges. Cultures appear to emerge in a high state of technical development and then decline after a period of time. Also associated with ancient cultures are concepts of astrology and an interest in astronomical measurement and the construction of large monuments for astronomical measurement. An interesting article illustrating this point and discussing ancient Inca culture states,

> A recent series of stunning archaeological finds in South America has revealed that the Incas were merely the final act in an Andean civilization that was far older and far more sophisticated than ever imagined. New excavations have turned up huge stone pyramids and other monuments that date back nearly 5,000 years, to about the time when the Great Pyramids were being constructed in Egypt.[6]

As the article discusses, even at its origin, Inca culture began with an already developed advanced technical capability. Elsewhere, in other geographical locations, a similar pattern is also discernible.

As is the case for the Incas, cultures around the world appear to have originated at about the same time of roughly five thousand years ago (three thousand B.C.). They appear with an already developed high level of

---

[6]William F. Allman with Joannie M. Schrof, "Lost Empires of the Americas" *U.S. News & World Report*, April 2, 1990, p. 46

technical development. Pyramids, for example, are not unique to Egypt, but a pyramid belt is found around the world, including the Americas and Asia. How are these things to be explained?

The puzzle is that there is little, if any, evidence to support the idea that these ancient cultures experimented with engineering designs. There is a lack of evidence pointing to a step-by-step development of the technology possessed by ancient cultures. Instead, each culture appears full-blown right from its beginning. Because of this lack of evidence for a trial-and-error developmental sequence, in the non-Biblical view it is assumed that an earlier society must have made the developments in a slow gradual evolutionary manner and it was then wiped out somehow by a catastrophe which destroyed any evidence of those developments.

What opinions does the secular world express about this puzzle? How do they attempt an explanation for the evidence? From an article on OOPArts in *Omni* magazine we read, "The unprecedented explosion of knowledge five thousand years ago, they believe, may have been foreshadowed by an earlier society whose cultural remnants have long since vanished."[7]

Some, such as Erich Von Däniken, have even suggested that ancient astronauts arrived on earth from other galaxies bringing their high technology with them.[8]

But the Biblical picture makes more sense. In a fascinating book discussing the accomplishments of ancient civilizations, one author succinctly summarizes,

[7]Robert Patton, "OOPARTS" *Omni*, September 1982, p. 54.

[8]Erich Von Däniken, *Chariots of the Gods?: Unsolved Mysteries of the Past*, New York, G. P. Putnam's Sons, 1969 (translated by Michael Heron).

A closer look at the strange artifacts now suggests that the ooparts originated in a man-made civilization - one that antedated known history - one that attained an elevated degree of development, but was destroyed to such an extent by a devastating catastrophe in the distant past that only a few remnants of its science and technology survived among the inferior cultures that succeeded it in history.[9]

We have seen that the evolutionary picture for the origin of man does not match with actual evidence. Evolutionism does not fit with reality. It does not fit the fossil record; it does not fit modern studies in molecular biology; it does not fit the study of human artifacts and, as we shall see, it does not fit with historical evidence either. A better picture is needed.

[9]Noorbergen, p. 3

CHAPTER II

BEGINNING
THE BIBLICAL PICTURE

F or man's origin, one of the two pictures on the puzzle box, the evolutionary one, is found to be unsatisfactory, as far as agreeing with factual evidence is concerned. In short, evolutionism simply does not agree with reality.

Other than naturalism (evolutionism), a supernatural explanation is the other possibility for man's origin and for that, the Biblical explanation is superior to all others. Although other creation accounts exist, the Biblical account best fits with reality. In our discussion of man's origin, our methodology will be based on taking Holy Scripture as the standard or measure of ultimate truth. "Therefore I esteem all thy precepts concerning all things to be right; and I hate every false way." (Psalm 119:128)

Methodology

What is involved methodologically in taking Scripture as the truth standard? Within modern Christendom there is much confusion about the place of Scripture and its use as a standard for truth. It is well therefore to explain here more fully what is meant and not meant by this methodology. In other words, how will this truth standard be applied?

In general, people use a mental filter for deciding or testing the truth or falsity of an idea. A person tends to reject from further consideration those ideas which do not pass his mental filter because they are viewed as not true. Those ideas which do not pass one's mental filter are rejected from further consideration because they are held to be not true. Most commonly a person's mental filter is largely developed from his surrounding culture. It is natural to assume that one's own culture is doing things the best possible way and according to truth. I first became aware of the assumptions people make about their own cultures when I began study of a foreign language. Common assumptions held by a culture are reflected in that culture's language, in its grammar rules, vocabulary and literature. The point was further emphasized to me during my travels to several foreign cultures. In most places, current culture is pagan, including current Western culture. Pagan culture is in a state of rebellion against the Creator and rejects His claims. It rejects Scripture as a standard or test of truth. Instead, the test of truth is usually the majority opinion of the surrounding culture.

However, upon Christian conversion, an individual's mental filter can be changed from the claims of pagan man as truth test to the Creator's written Word (The Holy Scriptures) as truth test. Conversion involves not only spiritual conversion, moral conversion, and emotional conversion, but it also involves intellectual conversion. "And be not conformed to this world: but be ye transformed by the renewing of your mind, that ye may prove what is that good, and acceptable, and perfect, will of God."[10]

Scripture has been communicated to man through revelation from the Creator and is therefore inerrant. The

[10]Romans 12:2

Creator does not lie and He has given us His written Word (The Holy Scriptures). Therefore, the methodology of this book is to take the Scriptures as the ultimate test of truth. That being said, we must also point out that on many topics, Scripture usually does not provide finer details. Additional sub-sets of assumptions and corollaries are needed for looking at and explaining details. Thus in treating any particular area of data, origins for example, it will usually be necessary to make additional assumptions. However when Scripture is taken as the absolute standard for ultimate truth, then any sub-corollaries and further assumptions which are made must agree and submit to the higher authority of Scripture.

Using this approach, an effort is made to assure that no preconception from the naturalism picture will be superimposed upon Scripture. Assumptions which are inherently in conflict with Scripture are excluded from consideration. This methodology of using Scripture as the ultimate test for truth means that man <u>can</u> know true truth in the absolute sense. It is possible to know truly even if not exhaustively, as some have so clearly pointed out.[11][12][13]

Now let us apply this methodology as we use Scripture as a better picture on the box.

Biblical Picture Summary

The Bible begins with Genesis 1:1 - "In the beginning God created the heaven and the earth." The entire

---

[11]Francis Schaeffer, *The God Who Is There: Speaking historic Christianity into the twentieth century*, Chicago, InterVarsity Press, 1968

[12]Francis Schaeffer, *He Is There and He Is Not Silent*

[13]J. Vernon McGee, *How To Interpret The Scripture*

universe and earth with its life forms including man are the result of direct acts of the Creator. Creation was supernatural, as opposed to a naturalistic process. In addition Scripture teaches that creation was *ex nihilo*, out of nothing. "For by him were all things created, that are in heaven, and that are in earth, visible and invisible, whether they be thrones, or dominions, or principalities, or powers: all things were created by him, and for him: And he is before all things, and by him all things consist."[14] "Through faith we understand that the worlds were framed by the word of God, so that things which are seen were not made of things which do appear."[15] The Creator did not need matter or energy or anything else. He is first. All else is second. All else is finite. Only the Creator is infinite. He is above all.

In the Bible and only in the Bible do we have creation *ex nihilo*. While there are other non-Biblical creation accounts, they all have a lower-grade creator who must use or assemble already available pre-existing materials. However the Creator revealed in Scripture is before all and above all and external to His creation.

The point of saying that the Creator is external to His creation is to differentiate clearly Biblical creation from pantheism. Pantheism equates god and the creation. The creation is god; god is the creation. Saying that the Creator is external to His creation does not mean that the Creator has barred Himself from access to the creation. Just the opposite is the case. The Biblical Creator lovingly and providentially cares for His creation. He interacts with it and guides it moment by

---

[14]Colossians 1:16-17

[15]Hebrews 11:3

moment, "... upholding all things by the word of His power." (Hebrews 1:3)

The Scriptural doctrine of creation *ex nihilo* has important philosophical and practical consequences. The list of consequences is a long one and to enumerate all of them would take more time and space than is appropriate here. We do, however, want to provide at least two examples. They will serve to illustrate the point that there are important consequences and further implications to any teaching about origins.

By way of illustration let us look at two consequences of the doctrine of creation *ex nihilo*. This doctrine leads directly to the idea that there are such things as absolutes and that there is a genuine, actual, and real external reality. External reality is not an illusion, but real. It was created by the Creator. Therefore the reference point for any absolute is the Creator Himself. Even those who deny the existence of absolutes and deny the existence of external reality are trapped by their own assertions. They insist it is absolute that there are no absolutes. It is apparent that such an insistence violates the law of non-contradiction. Those who insist on no external reality are confronted with absolute external reality in their daily living. If they are to continue living, they must <u>behave</u> as if there is an absolute external reality even while denying it. Even though one could deny the law of gravity, jumping from a cliff would not negate reality and the consequence of the jump. We all live in the Creator's world even if we wish to deny it. He sets the rules, not we who live in His world. The Creator is the absolute reference point.

The Scriptural teaching of a created and therefore genuine external non-illusory reality is also the basis for modern science. A basic assumption necessary for performing science is that there is a real external world which can be studied and experimented on. Creation *ex nihilo* is the philosophical basis that absolute truth exists. There are absolutes. Truth exists and it is absolute. It has an absolute reference point in the Creator who created the whole universe. Laws of thinking such as the law of non-contradiction in logic stem directly from the idea that there is a Creator who created a real external universe and placed man in the universe, allowing man to think about it. Some recent research provides interesting experimental evidence which documents the necessity of accepting external reality for carrying out thinking which is rational.[16] If there is no external reality, then thinking cannot be rational.

Scripture teaches that man was the highest and last of God's creation. After creating man, creation was finished and the Creator ended His work. It did not continue for millions of years. It was a finished and good creation. "And God saw every thing that he had made, and, behold, it was very good. And the evening and the morning were the sixth day."[17]

Chapter One of Genesis provides an overview or summary of creation. It identifies God: He is the Creator (In the beginning God created the heaven and the earth). Genesis One outlines for us the origin of the universe, the stars, the plant and animal life, and man, and ends with creation being finished.

When creation ended, the entire creation was in a state of perfection. Adam and Eve also were perfect in

---

[16]Bruce Bower, "Rational Mind Designs: Research into the ecology of thought treads on contested terrain" *Science News*, July 13, 1996, pp. 24-25

[17]Genesis 1:31

their original creation. They were fresh from the hand of the Creator and were in fellowship and in harmony with Him. They were in harmony with their surroundings, in harmony with each other, and in harmony internally (with themselves). Adam and Eve were in Paradise. They had not yet sinned and so had no motivation to hide from the Creator or from each other. They could be completely open with one another and could share one another's inmost thoughts. Even today in our fallen state it is exciting for a man and woman to fall in love. How much more so for Adam and Eve to be able to be completely "naked" or open with one another, to share their inmost being, to hide nothing. They had nothing to hide from one another or to be ashamed of. They were "naked and not ashamed." The Garden of Eden was truly a paradise. There were no tears of sorrow, no pain, no hassles, and no conflicts.

The Fall

Conditions in our world today however are vastly different from what they were in the Garden of Eden. As we observe our present world, we do not see one of peace and perfection. Instead we observe violence, death and decay, hassles, pain and tears. If the original creation was one of perfection, how did things get to be as they are now? What caused the change? Why all the evil in the world? How did it come about? Scripture explains what happened.

> Now the serpent was more subtil than any beast of the field which the LORD God had made. And he said unto the woman, Yea, hath God said, Ye shall not eat of every tree of the garden? And the woman said unto

the serpent, We may eat of the fruit of the trees of the garden: But of the fruit of the tree which is in the midst of the garden, God hath said, Ye shall not eat of it, neither shall ye touch it, lest ye die. And the serpent said unto the woman, Ye shall not surely die: For God doth know that in the day ye eat thereof, then your eyes shall be opened, and ye shall be as gods, knowing good and evil.[18]

Up until this point Adam and Eve's standard or test for truth was what the Creator had communicated to them. The Creator's Word, His verbal communication to Adam and Eve, served as their mental filter for testing the truthfulness of any statement. It was absolute and an accurate description of reality.

Now, however, that standard was being challenged. Adam and Eve were tempted to use <u>some</u> <u>other</u> <u>standard</u> for truth and they succumbed. That event, man setting himself up as decider and standard for truth, is commonly known as The Fall.

Initially, in reading the account of the Fall, a question came to my mind. Why was it so bad to eat that fruit? Yes, it was disobeying the Creator, but why was that so bad? For a long while, I concentrated on the fruit and missed the essential point. By concentrating on the fruit I totally missed what was occurring. It was far worse than eating that fruit. Notice what was happening. To Adam, the Creator had said, "Of every tree of the garden thou mayest freely eat: But of the tree of the knowledge of good and evil, thou shalt not eat of it: for in the day that thou eatest thereof thou shalt surely die." (Genesis 2:16-17) God spoke to Adam using the second person, singu-

[18]Genesis 3:1-5

lar case pronoun. He was speaking directly to Adam alone. Eve had not yet been created. After the creation of Eve, the Tempter questioned her about the Creator's command concerning eating of the fruit from the tree of the knowledge of good and evil. In her reply, Eve used the plural pronoun *we* referring to both herself and Adam. In his reply to Eve, the Tempter said, "Ye shall not surely die: For God doth know that in the day ye eat thereof, then your eyes shall be opened, and ye shall be as gods, knowing good and evil." The Tempter's statement, "Ye shall not surely die" is the exact opposite of what the Creator had said, "Thou shalt surely die." Somebody was lying. The temptation before Eve had two parts. Number One, the temptation was for Eve to believe that she herself had the right to decide who was telling the truth, the Creator, or some other source. Number Two, the temptation before Eve was for her to believe that she was smart enough to tell who was telling the truth, the Creator or some other source. To be able to tell whether the Creator is telling the truth, one must be as smart as the Creator. In effect, one must be God. The tempter stated to Eve, "Ye shall be as gods, knowing good and evil." The temptation was for Eve to be free from using the Creator's Word as standard for truth. It is to be noted that in addressing Eve, the Tempter also used the plural form of the second person pronoun. The statement, "Ye shall be as gods" was to convey to Eve the thought that both she and Adam could be equally gods.

At The Fall, man tried to elevate Himself to the status of God. He wanted to decide for himself what was true or not true, instead of submitting to the absolutes of the Creator. Since that time, mankind has been in rebellion against the Creator. As a result, people tend to erect intellectual systems to justify their rebellion. There are two approaches that people use. Either one will <u>think</u> his way into a pattern of living; or one will <u>live</u> his way into a pattern of thinking. Thus, since The Fall, man's natural tendency is to live his way into a pattern of thinking. In other words, he erects thinking patterns to justify the way he lives in rebellion against the Creator, rather than start with the Creator's rules and from them work out a pattern for living. All paradigms or explanations of origins other than Biblical Creation are attempts to avoid responsibility to the Creator. For current culture, naturalism is the philosophical and supposed scientific foundation or justification for these rationalizations.[19] It is well to note that naturalism (evolutionism) is not science; it is philosophy masquerading as science.

That same temptation is still being presented to people today. It is the same temptation that I faced. Each person is continually presented with the choice of either believing and obeying the Creator's Word or disobeying and moving to some other standard as source of truth. When I first began to consider the Biblical account as a possibility for assembling the puzzle pieces on origins, I was hit with the same temptation. I thought I had the right to decide whether The Creator's word, the Holy Bible, was true or not and I thought I was smart enough to make that decision. For example, I read that the Creator clearly said creation took place in seven days, but I asked (to myself), "Were these real, actual twenty-four-hour days?" I questioned the truth of the Creator's word.

---

[19]Henry Morris, *The Long War Against God: The History and Impact of the Creation/Evolution Conflict*, Grand Rapids, Baker Book House, 1989

Again, the temptation faced by Eve is the same temptation we all face today.

Consequences of the Fall

As a consequence of trusting some other standard of truth, Adam and Eve became estranged from the Creator and tried to hide from Him. Those consequences have been passed right on down to all humanity since. The natural tendency of all mankind is to trust some other standard for truth rather than Scripture, the Creator's Word. However, the Creator wouldn't lie to us. He loves us; He cares for us; He doesn't lie. The Creator spoke the truth when He said that there would be awful consequences for rejecting His Word as standard for truth. I've often wondered whether modern man's way of hiding from the Creator might not be to pretend that we weren't created. By pretending that we weren't created, man could therefore delude himself into believing that he was autonomous and not morally responsible to a Creator. He could live his way into a pattern of thinking and could generate his own standards of what is right and what is wrong and set his own standards for truth.

Adam and Eve, the first two people, were created in the image of the Creator. Contrary to naturalism's view of early man, they were not primitive. However, as a result of the Fall, man began to degenerate. At first, the degeneration was barely perceptible but its rate increased more and more with time, right up until the present day. The degeneration was not limited to man's physical body. Degeneration was in all areas: physical, mental, emotional, spiritual. Degeneration not only was upon man, but it applied to all of creation. "For the creature (read:

that which has been created or as we say now, the creation) was made subject to vanity, not willingly, but by reason of him who hath subjected the same in hope. Because the creature itself also shall be delivered from the bondage of corruption into the glorious liberty of the children of God. For we know that the whole creation groaneth and travaileth in pain together until now." (Romans 8:20-22) Degeneration applied not only to man, but also to the plant and animal kingdom and to all of creation as well. We are continuing to reap the terrible results of the Fall.

Scripture provides very few details on early history up until the time of the Flood. We often wish more details were provided, but they are not. What few details are given however, are significant details and provide an overview of people and events. These few details allow us to make intelligent guesses as to what a more complete picture would look like. We can work at filling in the gaps.

As a consequence of the Fall, Adam's body began to age and degenerate until eventually he died physically. The last thing we read about Adam is, "he lived 930 years and he died." (Genesis 5:5) Doubters attempting to find errors in Scripture sometimes assert that the statement of Adam's dying at age 930 years is one example of many errors in the Bible. They base this assertion from what the Creator said to Adam concerning eating the forbidden fruit: "And the LORD God commanded the man, saying, Of every tree of the garden thou mayest freely eat: But of the tree of the knowledge of good and evil, thou shalt not eat of it: for in the day that thou eatest thereof thou shalt surely die." (Genesis 2:16-17)

The skeptic asserts that Adam did not die the very day he partook of the forbidden fruit, but lived on for over nine hundred more years afterwards. Therefore they think these statements are an example of an error.

However it is the skeptic who is in error, not the Creator. The Creator had stated, "the day that thou eatest thereof thou shalt *surely die*. In Hebrew, the statement "surely die" carries the meaning of strong emphasis. The Creator was emphatic about the consequences if Adam disobeyed. In Hebrew the text literally reads, "dying thou shalt die." Hebrew uses that grammatical construction as an idiom to communicate strong emphasis. That same pattern is used elsewhere in the Hebrew Old Testament.

An example illustrating this point is found in a passage from the prophet Isaiah. The Lord said to Isaiah, "Go, and tell this people, Hear ye indeed, but understand not; and see ye indeed, but perceive not." (Isaiah 6:9) Here the English word *indeed* is used to show emphasis. The verbs hear and see are emphatic in the original Hebrew. Literally the Hebrew is "hearing ye shall hear and seeing ye shall see." They did hear and see indeed; they surely did hear and see. In quoting this passage from Isaiah, the Apostle Paul renders it, "Go unto this people, and say, Hearing ye shall hear, and shall not understand; and seeing ye shall see, and not perceive" (Acts 28:26) Jesus also quoted the same passage from Isaiah, "And in them is fulfilled the same prophecy of Esaias, which saith, by hearing ye shall hear, and shall not understand; and seeing ye shall see, and not perceive." (Matt. 13:13-14) Jesus preached and preached and preached. He also did miracle after miracle. They really heard and they really saw! In effect, the Creator was saying to Adam, "You shall absolutely, indeed, truly, really die." It was not just a passing remark the Creator mentioned to Adam, but one of strong emphasis.

Upon eating the forbidden fruit, man as he had been created to be, that very moment no longer existed. He died. Man was created to be in harmony with his Creator, in harmony with others, in harmony with the environment and in harmony internally with himself. Adam died when he ate the fruit. True, Adam, though dead, still possessed physical life, but even that was now degenerating and eventually resulted in physical death as well. Adam as he was created to be, no longer existed. Adam died, not 930 years later, but that very day. Of course he also experienced physical death 930 years later. The fact that "death" as used by the Creator meant more than just physical death is in agreement with the remarks of Jesus when he said, "let the dead bury their dead." (Matthew 8:22) It is possible to be physically alive and yet be spiritually dead, and therefore dead compared with man as originally created.

Now, subsequent to the Fall, in order to regain life and be more than just physically alive, one must be born again. Again Jesus emphasized this point very strongly as recorded for us in his discussion with Nicodemus, one of the great Jewish scholars of Jesus' time.

> There was a man of the Pharisees, named Nicodemus, a ruler of the Jews: The same came to Jesus by night, and said unto him, Rabbi, we know that thou art a teacher come from God: for no man can do these miracles that thou doest, except God be with him. Jesus answered and said unto him, Verily, verily, I say

unto thee, Except a man be born again, he cannot see the kingdom of God. Nicodemus saith unto him, How can a man be born when he is old? can he enter the second time into his mother's womb, and be born? Jesus answered, Verily, verily, I say unto thee, Except a man be born of water and of the Spirit, he cannot enter into the kingdom of God. That which is born of the flesh is flesh; and that which is born of the Spirit is spirit. Marvel not that I said unto thee, Ye must be born again. (John 3:1-7)

Born Again

How does one become "born again?" At the Fall, man's nature was changed and that has affected every human being since. All human beings now have a natural tendency to do what is wrong rather than what is right. Our natural state is one of rebellion against the Creator. We are naturally spiritually dead and must be born again in order to become fully alive again in the same sense that Adam and Eve were originally. Spiritual life can again become a reality even though full restoration to perfection will not be achieved in this life. Yet there are tremendous advantages available even in this life to those who are truly born again.

How then can one be born again? The answer is by following the Creator's recipe for it. The Creator's recipe is in the Savior, His only begotten Son.

For God so loved the world, that he gave his only begotten Son, that whosoever believeth in him should not perish, but have everlasting life. For God sent not his Son into the world to condemn the world; but that the world through him might be saved. He that

believeth on him is not condemned: but he that
believeth not is condemned already, because he hath
not believed in the name of the only begotten Son of
God. And this is the condemnation, that light is come
into the world, and men loved darkness rather than
light, because their deeds were evil. For everyone that
doeth evil hateth the light, neither cometh to the
light, lest his deeds should be reproved. But he that
doeth truth cometh to the light, that his deeds may be
made manifest, that they are wrought in God." (John
3:16-21)

The Creator's recipe is to believe Him, confess our sins to
Him and repent of our old dead ways. "That if thou
shalt confess with thy mouth the Lord Jesus, and shalt
believe in thine heart that God hath raised him from the
dead, thou shalt be saved." (Romans 10:9-10) The
Creator was not caught by surprise when man fell; He
already had arranged for a Savior.

Although the literal Hebrew is the expression, "dying
thou shalt die" and is an idiom for showing emphasis for
the word *die*, it can also have a literal fulfillment as well.
The very day that Adam ate the fruit, his body began the
continuing degenerative process of dying, resulting
eventually in a literal physical death. It can also have an
application to all of subsequent humanity in general. All
of mankind has continued to degenerate ever since the
Fall of Adam and Eve. Inherited diseases and deformities,
the appearance of new diseases, environmental degrada-
tion, decreased longevity are all too evident and apply to
all of mankind.

Because we now live in a fallen world, it is easy to fall
into the trap of thinking that everyday occurrences as

they happen in a now-fallen and degenerating world are normal. Thus we accept aging and death as "normal," but they are not. Death is abnormal. We were not created to die. You have a right to cry at a funeral. Funerals are an ever-present reminder that we live in a fallen and degenerating world.

In this chapter we have seen that the Biblical picture begins with earth's first two people living in a completed and perfect creation. Now, however, things obviously are not perfect. The Bible explains why. As a result of the Fall, man chose to reject the Creator's word as standard for truth and all of creation began a process of degeneration. Man was created, but has since fallen and now needs a savior. A Savior is provided: the Lord Jesus Christ.

How does the Biblical picture relate to answering the puzzle of man's origins and the puzzle of ancient artifacts? Let us take Scriptural hints and begin building a picture for ancient man. That means we will need to examine some of the details from man's past.

CHAPTER III

ANTE-DILUVIAN TECHNOLOGY

Now that we have provided an overview of the Biblical picture, we are ready to look at some details. Even though the early people of the earth, Adam and Eve and their descendants, were in a fallen and degenerating state, they were not "primitive" people. Being closer to Creation than we are, they had not degenerated as far as we have. Their bodies were far more perfect, their minds more alert and capable, and their lifetimes longer. With their good health, keen observational powers and alert minds, they soon began to develop a high level of science and technology. It is an error to assume, as current culture does, that early man was not mentally highly capable or that he was ignorant of what we would call science and scientific principles.

Pre-Flood Agriculture, Arts and Science

Although numerous intriguing examples of ancient artifacts have been discovered, exact dating of them remains imprecise. These artifacts certainly do reflect advanced science and engineering skills. Some investigators have suggested that some of these ancient artifacts may actually date to pre-Flood times. While that may be a possibility, dating of these objects is as yet too imprecise to be certain. Probably in most cases they are from post-Flood times.

Nevertheless, some reflection of the high technical achievements of mankind even before the Flood is hinted at in the passage of Genesis 4:20-22.

> And Adah bare Jabal: he was the father of such as dwell in tents, and of such as have cattle. And his brother's name was Jubal: he was the father of all such as handle the harp and organ. And Zillah, she also bare Tubal-cain, an instructer of every artificer in brass and iron...

From this passage we observe that in just seven generations from Adam, early man had made significant developments. Antediluvians were not barely surviving as primitive hunters living in caves as the naturalism picture would have us believe. Instead they carried on organized agriculture including animal husbandry. Verse twenty mentions cattle. In the Bible the word *cattle* refers not just to bovines, as for example milk cows or beef animals, but to domesticated animals in general. Sheep and goats would also be included in this term.

Continuing with the list of antediluvian accomplishments we find that "Jubal was the father of all such as handle the harp and organ." Music was clearly a part of the culture, as indicated by mention of both stringed and wind instruments. Although we cannot be certain about exact dates, archaeologists have uncovered musical instruments from very ancient times.[20] Some of these ancient instruments are not crude or "primitive," but are highly crafted. Even with our modern technology we do not know how these ancient instruments might be improved

---

[20] "Neandertal noisemaker" *Science News*, November 23, 1996, p. 328

to make better music. Evidence indicates that music itself is very ancient.[21]

Early metallurgy is described in Genesis 4:22. Tubal-cain was an "instructor of every artificer of brass and iron." Here "brass" comes from the Hebrew word meaning base or common metals such as copper, as opposed to the more valuable noble metals such as silver or gold.[22] The term "brass" could also include alloys of base metals. Bronze, for example, is an alloy composed mostly of the metals copper and tin. Some popular modern translations do, in fact, render the word here as "bronze."[23] Although some metals can be directly mined from the earth in metallic form and may not require much technical sophistication for their production, others do require knowledge of higher technology such as a smelting process. The smelting and refining of metals from their ores is indicated in Genesis 4:22. While metallic copper may sometimes be mined directly as from deposits of native copper, metallic iron must be smelted. For iron the smelting process requires fairly complex chemical knowledge. If these early people could smelt iron from its ore, they most certainly could also smelt copper from its ore because it is easier to smelt copper than iron. The production and forging of iron requires fairly sophisticated technical skills. We are led to conclude that the early peoples developed skills in agriculture, animal husbandry, science and the arts.

---

[21]Urana Clarke, "How Our Music Began" *The Book of Knowledge* (Volume 18) New York, 1957, pp. 6695-6700.

[22]James Strong, "Hebrew and Chaldee Dictionary" *Strong's Exhaustive Concordance of the Bible*, New York, Abingdon-Cokesbury Press, 1890, p. 78, #5178.

[23]New International Version, New American Standard

Evolutionary archaeologists have attempted to organize human history in terms of various supposed 'ages' — Stone Age, Bronze Age, Iron Age, etc. The Noahic record, however, indicates that early men were very competent in both brass and iron metallurgy, as well as agriculture, animal husbandry, and urbanization. It is significant that many kinds of bronze and iron implements are known to have been used in the earliest civilizations of Sumeria and Egypt. The same is true of musical instruments, and it is evident that the science and art of metallurgy and music had been handed down from ancient times to these earliest post-Flood civilizations. Modern archaeology is confirming the high degree of technology associated with the earliest human settlers all over the world.[24]

"I believe that it is possible to say with a high degree of confidence that a well-developed bronze technology was present in mainland Southeast Asia prior to 2000 B.C."[25]

Archaeologists once thought that Bronze Age people got their metals largely by chipping away at surface rocks; at most, they would tunnel only a few dozen feet. The newly discovered mine shows that the Bronze Age miners were far more skilled and adventurous than that. Located at the base of towering, 2,200-ft. red sandstone cliffs, the mine contains a complex, multilevel network of some 200 shafts and galleries. ... Bronze Age miners were able to produce

---

[24]Henry Morris, *The DEFENDER'S Study Bible*, Grand Rapids, World Publishing, 1995, p. 17.

[25]D. T. Bayard, "Early Thai Bronze: Analysis and New Dates" *Science*, 30 June 1972, p. 1412.

22-lb. copper ingots that were 97% to 98% pure, a
degree of purity not exceeded until modern times.[26]

Mental Capability

The process of degeneration which began at the Fall
affected all areas. It seems reasonable to conclude that
not only was man's physical body affected, but also his
mental powers as well. Suppose, for the sake of argu-
ment, that because of the Fall, mankind's average intelligence level has been decreasing. However, at a time closer
to creation, mental degeneration had not progressed as
far as at present. Yet, even with diminished mental
capability, modern man's scientific and technical achievements are impressive. Extrapolating backwards to the
time before the Flood and much closer to Creation,
mankind's average mental capability was surely at least
equal to that of our own modern times, and was in fact
probably greater.

Then combine this degree of mental capability with
the fact that the average life span of people who lived
before the Flood was also much greater. Their life span
was many hundreds of years, even coming close to a
thousand years. With their alert minds, keen observational powers, good health, longevity, and common
language, it should not be surprising that they were able
to develop an advanced technology.

As already stated, the passage in Genesis 4:20-22
refers to advanced technology at a time only seven generations removed from Adam's creation. If people had
already advanced this far so early in their development of

---

[26]"The Oldest Mine?" *Time*, January 13, 1975, p. 65.

civilization, organized agriculture, musical instruments, and metallurgy, what could they have developed in the many remaining years before Noah's Flood? May I suggest for consideration that by the time of Noah's Flood, they may well have developed a level of science and technology that we haven't matched until the twentieth century or even possibly that we may not yet have attained. Later chapters will provide further support for this suggestion.

Pre-Flood Social Conditions

Why does the Bible not spend more time discussing pre-Flood technological achievements? No doubt God had good reason not to tell us very much about it. Perhaps it was because their scientific and technological achievements were eclipsed by their almost unbelievable moral and spiritual bankruptcy. "And GOD saw that the wickedness of man was great in the earth, and that every imagination of the thoughts of his heart was only evil continually." (Genesis 6:5) They were involved in depravity that was so abnormal and so unnatural that every imagination of their heart was only evil continually. In discussing pre-Flood conditions during Noah's day, Jesus stated, "They did eat, they drank, they married wives, they were given in marriage, until the day that Noe entered into the ark, and the flood came, and destroyed them all." (Luke 17:27) In other words, they were preoccupied with physical appetites. Continuing, Jesus then stated, "Likewise also as it was in the days of Lot; they did eat, they drank, they bought, they sold, they planted, they builded..." (Luke 17:28) This passage informs us that they were also preoccupied with materialism. They were continually in pursuit of material possessions. In rejecting the Creator and His authority, the pre-Flood population became corrupt. "And God looked upon the earth, and, behold, it was corrupt; for all flesh had corrupted his way upon the earth." (Genesis 6:12)

Even restricting ourselves to the technology associated with those items listed in Genesis 4:20-22, how was that early high technology used? Sadly, we read in Genesis 6:11 and 13, "The earth also was corrupt before God, and the earth was filled with violence. And God said unto Noah, the end of all flesh is come before me; for the earth is filled with violence through them; and, behold, I will destroy them with the earth." They used their high science and technology to fill the world with violence. Our term for using technology to generate violence is war. The Creator intended people to live in peace with each other. But the antediluvians flagrantly violated the Creator's intent. Man then, as now, is fallen and is in rebellion against the Creator. As a consequence, the whole world was filled with violence and evil. Genesis 6:5 - "And GOD saw that the wickedness of man was great in the earth, and that every imagination of the thoughts of his heart was only evil continually."

Advance Warning of Flood

One of the amazing attributes of the Creator is His graciousness. In spite of man's rebellion and evil activity, the Creator remains gracious. In pre-Flood times, the Creator warned mankind not to behave in an evil manner. "...But (God) saved Noah the eighth person, a preacher of righteousness, bringing in the Flood upon the world of the ungodly" (II Peter 2:5). To that evil generation, the Creator sent Noah as a preacher of righteousness. Noah preached that men should repent from their evil ways and live righteously. He warned of a coming judgment. Even though rebellious man deserves the Creator's judgment, the Creator is gracious and provides warnings and a way to escape. "And the LORD said, My spirit shall not always strive with man, for that he also is flesh: yet his days shall be an hundred and twenty years." (Genesis 6:3) Noah preached righteousness and warned of coming judgment. He had up to one hundred and twenty years to do that. Everyone on earth had an opportunity to hear that warning and to escape the Flood, but the warning was ignored.

Noah also constructed the Ark during this time. The building of the Ark was an object lesson to all who observed, that Noah was serious about the message he was preaching. From this portion of Scripture alone we cannot be certain of the exact amount of time actually used for construction of the Ark. Construction may have been carried on for the entire one hundred and twenty years, or for some shorter period. In any case, the Creator provided adequate advance warning. Also, since Noah was <u>at least</u> as smart as we are, the construction of the Ark needn't have taken him an extremely long time.

What is the meaning of the phrase in Genesis 6:3, "his days shall be an hundred and twenty years?" Contrary to what one might assume at first glance, it does not indicate the lifetime or longevity to which people would be reduced. Instead it is a prophecy of the remaining years until the Flood would occur. It is clear that the one hundred twenty years could not refer to longevity because even after the Flood, lifetimes were far in excess of that. Noah continued to live an additional 350 years.

"And Noah lived after the flood three hundred and fifty years." (Genesis 9:28) Also Noah's sons, grandsons, and great-grandsons had lifespans far longer than one hundred twenty years. Although lifetimes after the Flood were being greatly reduced, they were still much greater than one hundred twenty. Abraham lived to one hundred seventy-five years and Isaac to one hundred eighty years. Moses, many years later lived to one hundred twenty years. However, by the time of King David, lifetimes had decreased to approximately seventy years. (Psalm 90:10) Thus we see clearly that the one hundred twenty years of Genesis 6:3 was the lead-time the Creator in grace provided mankind in which to repent before the coming judgment of the Flood. All mankind had over a century of warning that the Flood was coming.

Noah is in fact one of my heroes. He was not only a righteous man and a man of faith, but also of courage. He preached, but was scoffed at and ridiculed. The surrounding culture was overwhelmingly opposed to his righteous style of life and to his message. I can imagine what it must have been like for him. He preached that it was going to rain.

Some believe that mankind up to this point had never experienced rain. They suggest that meteorological conditions before the Flood may have been a continuation of those suggested in Genesis 2:5-6.

> And every plant of the field before it was in the earth, and every herb of the field before it grew: for the LORD God had not caused it to rain upon the earth, and there was not a man to till the ground. But there went up a mist from the earth, and watered the whole face of the ground.

If this is the case and Noah preached that the event of the Flood would include rain, then these events were totally outside of the realm of mankind's experience. Most of the water from the Flood probably did not result from rain, but from the opening up of the fountains of the great deep. However, rain was included.

"By faith Noah, being warned of God of things not seen as yet, moved with fear, prepared an ark to the saving of his house; by the which he condemned the world, and became heir of the righteousness which is by faith." (Hebrews 11:7) They did not know what it was to have rain associated with a breaking up of the fountains of the great deep to produce a global flood. The entire prophesied event was outside of normal events and processes experienced by the antediluvians. Those in rebellion against the Creator have a tendency to scoff at that which they do not know or understand, especially when it comes from the Creator. "But the natural man receiveth not the things of the Spirit of God: for they are foolishness unto him: neither can he know them, because they are spiritually discerned." (I Corinthians 2:14)

Thus I can envision a scenario somewhat as follows. As Noah was building the Ark, a scoffer probably asked him why he was building the Ark. Noah may have replied, "Because it is going to rain." They did not know what rain was, so they then probably asked what rain was. Noah replied, "Rain is water coming down out of the sky." Since they had not experienced water dropping from the sky, they may have ridiculed Noah even further: "Water coming out of the sky?? Oh, Noah, how crazy can you get?" Then to scoff even further, they said, "Hey, Noah, we would like to have you try a little scientific experiment. Hold your hand up into the sky. Now pull it down and examine it. Does your hand look wet? And furthermore, you have been saying such crazy things for over one hundred and nineteen years! What a fanatic you are!" Noah is one of my great heroes. He continued to preach and warn while building the ark, even in the face of scoffing.

One of the things which has impressed me while reading the Holy Scriptures is that when the Creator says something is going to happen within a certain time, as we continue reading, we find that it happened. Thus for Noah's time, we read,

> And it came to pass after seven days, that the waters of the flood were upon the earth. ... And all flesh died that moved upon the earth, both of fowl, and of cattle, and of beast, and of every creeping thing that creepeth upon the earth, and every man: All in whose nostrils was the breath of life, of all that was in the dry land, died. And every living substance was destroyed which was upon the face of the ground, both man, and cattle, and the creeping things, and the fowl of the heaven; and they were destroyed from the earth: and Noah only remained alive, and they that were with him in the ark. (Genesis 7:10, 21-23)

Just as the Creator had warned that it would, the Flood came and totally destroyed all of the antediluvian civilization. It totally wiped out and destroyed all of that technology, but it did not destroy its memory. When Noah and his family came out of the Ark, they had to rebuild, but they did not have to reinvent or rediscover the pre-Flood technology. They already knew that those things could be done. What became of that knowledge after the Flood? Would the post-diluvians reapply any of that knowledge?

NIMROD'S KINGDOM

Before the Flood, an advanced civilization incorpo
rating much technical knowledge had been
developed. Although that civilization and its
technology was destroyed by the Flood, the memory of
pre-Flood culture and its achievements was not lost. Let
us now look at what developed in post-diluvian times.

Figure 1 The Land of Shinar (Mesopotamia)

The Ark landed in the "mountains of Ararat" in the
Middle East. (Genesis 8:4) Mt. Ararat is located between
the Black and the Caspian seas in the present-day coun-
try of Turkey.

After leaving the Ark, most if not all of Noah's early
descendants migrated to the land of Shinar, or

Mesopotamia, or Babylonia as it eventually became known, and dwelt there.

The Creator's post-flood command

Again, after the Flood, the Creator provided mankind with a specific instruction to be obeyed as recorded in Genesis 9:1. "And God blessed Noah and his sons, and said unto them, Be fruitful, and multiply, and replenish the earth." In other words, God's command was for man to scatter out and not to congregate all together in one place. This was God's specific command to man after the Flood.

The word translated replenish as used in Genesis 9:1 appears only two places in Scripture and is exactly the same Hebrew word in both places. In addition to appearing in Genesis 9:1, replenish also appears in the creation account, Genesis 1:28. The Creator's command to His newly created couple was to be fruitful and replenish the earth. As is well known, words often change in meaning over time. Replenish is translated from a Hebrew word meaning to fill or to fill fully or completely.[27] In 1611 when the Authorized Version was published, replenish meant the same in English as the Hebrew word from which it was translated. However over the intervening years, the "re" of replenish has come to mean "again." A modern reader not aware of this fact would erroneously read replenish as meaning to fill again.

> The Hebrew word translated "replenish" simply means "fill" — not "refill"! The Hebrew word occurs 306 times in the Old Testament and in not one instance does it mean "refill." ... An examination of

---

[27]Strong, p. 66, #4390

the Oxford English dictionary shows the English word "replenish" was used to mean "fill" from the 13th to the 17th centuries. In no case, during these five centuries does it mean "refill."[28]

From Genesis 9:18-19 we read, "And the sons of Noah, that went forth of the ark, were Shem, and Ham, and Japheth: and Ham is the father of Canaan. These are the three sons of Noah: and of them was the whole earth overspread." Thus according to the Scriptural picture, all peoples on earth today are descended from Noah and his three sons, Shem, Ham, and Japheth. As discussed in Chapter 15, modern biochemical analysis appears to support this idea. Research with mitochondrial DNA and genetics connects mankind's lineage back to one woman and one man. All can trace their lineage back to Noah and his family, and then through them back originally to Adam and Eve.

Although secular scientific literature acknowledges mankind's origin from only one man and one woman, secular authors are highly uncomfortable with that idea, especially as it relates to the time scale reported since the one man and one woman were alive. Although varying slightly between different authors, secular literature originally reported a date of about two hundred thousand years. This reported date is uncomfortably closer to the traditional Biblical time line of several thousand years, rather than the millions of years naturalistic philosophy (evolutionism) usually associates with the origin of man. As a result, those who believe in naturalism attempt to push back as far as possible the date for the

---

[28]"Did You Know" *Acts & Facts*, February 1990, page "c"

first man and woman. But such attempts encounter problems when faced with historical data. Further comments on the Biblical time scale and the origin of man will be made in Chapter 15.

The Table of Nations

Continuing with the history of mankind after the Flood, we come to Genesis chapter ten, a very important document. It is known as the Table of Nations because it traces for us how the descendants of Shem, Ham, and Japheth developed into the various tribes, peoples and nations now on earth. A recently published scholarly and in-depth study of actual historical and genealogical records from sources outside the Bible shows that these records agree with the Bible in amazing detail.[29]

Chapter ten of Genesis begins, "Now these are the generations of the sons of Noah, Shem, Ham, and Japheth: and unto them were sons born after the flood." Let us look now at Genesis 10:6, 8 and 10: "And the sons of Ham were Cush..." Cush was Noah's grandson. "Cush begat Nimrod: he began to be a mighty one in the earth." This means he was politically powerful as is explained in verses nine and ten, "He was a mighty hunter before the LORD: wherefore it is said, Even as Nimrod the mighty hunter before the LORD. And the beginning of his kingdom was Babel, and Erech, and Accad, and Calneh in the land of Shinar." The land of Shinar is also known as Babylonia or Mesopotamia. Secular history attests to the Akkadian empire which is the same as the Biblical kingdom of Accad.

---

[29]Bill Cooper, *After The Flood: The Early Post-Flood History of Europe*, New Wine Press, West Sussex, England, 1995

Nimrod was the world's first dictator. He was a rebel against the Creator's post-flood design that there should be a multiplicity of local governments and units instead of one world government. (Genesis 9:1; Acts. 17:26-28) In fact, Nimrod's name means "Let us rebel."[30] An interesting item in the British Museum is a bust of an ancient ruler in Mesopotamia. Because of the age attributed to this bust, this may well be a bust of Nimrod; we can't be absolutely certain. According to historians, the Sargonoid or Akkadian empire (Nimrod's empire) lasted until about 2200 B.C.

One scholar who has specialized in studies of ancient Babylonia has written his impressions of some of the reasons for Nimrod's political power.

> The amazing extent of the worship of this man indicates something very extraordinary in his character; and there is ample reason to believe, that in his own day he was an object of high popularity. Though by setting up as king, Nimrod invaded the patriarchal system, and abridged the liberties of mankind, yet he was held by many to have conferred benefits upon them, that amply indemnified them for the loss of their liberties, and covered him with glory and renown. ... The exploits of Nimrod, therefore, in hunting down the wild beasts of the field, and ridding the world of monsters, must have gained for him the character of a pre-eminent benefactor of his race. By this means, not less than by the bands he trained, was his power acquired, when he *first* began to be mighty upon the earth; and in the same way, no doubt, was that power consolidated. ... Within the battlements of

---

[30] Henry M. Morris, *The DEFENDER'S Study Bible*, note on Genesis 10:8, p. 29.

a fortified city no such danger from savage animals was to be dreaded; and for the security afforded in this way, men no doubt looked upon themselves as greatly indebted to Nimrod. No wonder, therefore, that the name of the 'mighty hunter,' who was at the same time the prototype of 'the god of fortifications,' should have become a name of renown.[31]

The Creator intended for man to move out into the post-Flood environs in an organized, ordered manner, just as the Israelites were intended to move through the wilderness and into the Promised Land. However, Nimrod had a lust for power and set about building a centralized government and power structure in direct defiance of the Creator's command.

Another author also summarizes the importance of Nimrod.

Nimrod was undoubtedly the most notorious man in the ancient world who is credited with instigating the Great Rebellion at Babel, and of founding the very worst features of paganism, including the practice of magical arts, astrology and even human sacrifice. Moreover, there is much evidence to suggest that he himself was worshipped from the very earliest times. ... One of the chief cities of Assyria was named **Nimrud**, and the Plain of Shinar, known to the Assyrians as Sen'ar and the site of the Great Rebellion, was itself known as the Land of Nimrod.[32]

---

[31]Rev. Alexander Hislop, *The Two Babylons*, Neptune NJ, Loizeaux Brothers, 1959, p. 50-51.

[32]Cooper, *After The Flood: The Early Post-Flood History of Europe*, New Wine Press, West Sussex, England, 1995, p. 189-190.

The Earth was divided

Genesis 10:25 describes an important event in the history of the early post-Flood world. "And unto Eber were born two sons: the name of the one was Peleg; for in his days was the earth divided; and his brother's name was Joktan." Any event mentioned in these early chapters of Genesis is significant because these first eleven chapters cover roughly the first two thousand years of history while all of the rest of the Bible covers roughly the next two thousand years. Thus any event mentioned in Genesis 1-11 is of special significance.

In Peleg's day the earth was divided. This is the only place in the Table of Nations where both the son's name and also the meaning of the name are given, indicating the importance of the event Peleg's name commemorated. Some commentators have suggested that the <u>earth divided</u> refers to the confusion of language and the scattering of peoples from Babel. As support for this idea they cite (Genesis 10:5) "By these were the isles of the Gentiles divided in their lands; every one after his tongue, after their families, in their nations." and (Genesis 10:32) "These are the families of the sons of Noah, after their generations, in their nations: and by these were the nations divided in the earth after the flood."

However two different words for division are used, *pelag* in Genesis 10:25 and *parad* in Genesis 10:5 and 32, suggesting a different type of division.[33] Because a different word is used for the division of Peleg's day than for events associated with Babel, many other commentators

---

[33]Henry Morris, *The DEFENDER'S Study Bible*, World Publishing, Grand Rapids, 1995, p. 31.

have suggested that the passage may mean something other than a scattering of peoples from Babel. Instead, they suggest that Genesis 10:25 might refer to splitting of the continents from a single large post-Flood continent. There are several problems with this suggestion, however. One problem concerns the sheer magnitude of a geological event large enough to result in the breakup of a single large landmass into our present continents. Such an event would have been nearly as catastrophic as the Flood itself. Large amounts of water from ocean basins would most likely have suddenly washed over the land surfaces with devastating effects on animal and plant life. As one commentator remarks concerning this interpretation,

> Many Bible teachers have suggested, therefore, that Genesis 10:25 might refer to a splitting of the single post-Flood continent into the present continents of the world. They associate the modern scientific model of sea-floor spreading and continental drifting with Genesis 10:25. It should be remembered, however, that the continental drift hypothesis has by no means been proved, and the verse seems to refer more directly to the division into families, countries and languages. Furthermore, even if the continents have separated from a single primeval continent, such a split more likely would have occurred in connection with the continental uplifts terminating the global deluge. (Psalm 104:6-9).[34]

A third possibility for the meaning of the earth divided seems more likely, especially in view of the meaning of the original Hebrew word translated into

[34]Morris, 1995, p. 31

English as "divided." The particular word used for division in Genesis 10:25 occurs only three times in the entire Bible. The first occurrence is Genesis 10:25 which we have already quoted above.

A second occurrence appears in I Chronicles and is almost identical to the first occurrence in Genesis. "And unto Eber were born two sons: the name of the one was Peleg; because in his days the earth was divided: and his brother's name was Joktan." (I Chronicles 1:19) Here the meaning of divided is the same as in the Genesis 10:25 passage.

The third and last occurrence of the Hebrew word translated "divided" is in Job 38:25, "Who hath divided a watercourse for the overflowing of waters, or a way for the lightning of thunder." The Creator divided a watercourse for the overflowing of waters. In context the Hebrew from which this is translated refers to channels in which water for rivers was to flow, or to surveyed, man-made canals for carrying irrigation water. In other words, the Creator marked off courses for rivers or canals, or as we more commonly phrase it, the Creator surveyed courses for, or boundaries for, these watercourses. This explanation is in agreement not only with the meaning of Peleg in Hebrew, but also its meaning in Akkadian and Assyrian usages of the word at that time.[35]

In his scholarly work on the table of nations Cooper says,

> Peleg: Genesis tells us that in his day the earth was divided. The meaning of his name, as rendered in

---

[35]see gush or flood 7858, a channel 8585 in Strong's Concordance

Hebrew, corresponds exactly with the Akkadian noun
<u>pulukku</u>, which means a dividing up of territory by
means of boundaries and borders (the Akkadian verb
for 'to divide' is palaku). Likewise, the Assyrian word,
<u>palgu</u>, refers to the dividing up of land by canals and
irrigation systems. It is in this sense that the Hebrew
word peleg is used in Job 29:6 and 38:5. The man
named Peleg, (whose name appears as <u>Phaleg</u> in
Josephus), was so named, however, after the division
and scattering of the nations from Babel. In fact, one
of the ancient names of Babylon (Babel) is nowadays
translated as 'the place of canals', though surely a
better translation would be 'the place of division', or
even the place of Peleg. There is an ancient city that
bore the name of Peleg, however, the Akkadian town
of Phalgu, whose ruins lie at the junction of the
Euphrates and Chaboras rivers (Chebar, see Ezekiel
1:1). Of further interest to us is the fact that the
division of the nations is recorded in Genesis as
occurring in the fifth generation after the Flood. We
will encounter striking confirmation of this when we
study the descent of certain European kings later.[36]

Thus the third meaning of the phrase "the earth was
divided" seems to fit best. It is equivalent to our modern
word *surveyed*. After the Flood, in Peleg's day, the earth
was surveyed to locate necessary resources for building
the post-Flood civilization.

Genesis chapter eleven continues with the account of
what was occurring under Nimrod as dictator. We read
in verse 1, "And the whole earth was of one language and
one speech." That there was a time when everyone spoke

---

[36]Cooper, *After The Flood: The Early Post-Flood History of Europe*, New Wine Press,
West Sussex, England, 1995, pp. 177-178

the same language is not unique to the Bible. Other data from extra-Biblical sources also support this idea.

> It is interesting that a tradition of a universal language seems to be common in ancient literature. In Genesis we read, of course, 'And the whole earth was of one language and one speech.' Lincoln Barnett, in his *Treasure of Our Tongue*, remarks, 'The notion that at one time all men spoke a single language is by no means unique to Genesis. It found expression in ancient Egypt, in early Hindu and Buddhist writings and was seriously explored by several European philosophers during the 16th Century....'[37]

It is not surprising that everyone spoke the same language. The vocabulary and grammar was that of Noah and his family. Noah's family spoke the language of the antediluvians and scholars have noted that it may have been similar to Hebrew. Henry Morris, for example, comments,

> Literally, 'of one lip and one set of words' — that is, one phonology and one vocabulary, the same language as spoken by the antediluvians. This may well have been the Hebrew language, or some similar Semitic language since the primitive records were transmitted through Noah and Shem and since it is very unlikely that either Noah or Shem were participants in the rebellion and judgment at Babel.[38]

With the entire post-Flood population speaking a common language, there was little to hinder a rapid

[37]Charles Hapgood, *Maps of the Ancient Sea Kings*, p. 204

[38]Henry Morris, *The DEFENDER'S Study Bible*, World Publishing, Grand Rapids, 1995, p. 31.

rebuilding and development of technology. What indicators exist for the re-development of civilization after the Flood?

CHAPTER V

BRONZE AGE EXPLORERS

E vidence of worldwide exploration, trade, and communication in ancient times has been hinted at by numerous authors. For example, an encyclopedia, when discussing the origin of music, points out that not only is music very ancient, but that early music form, style, and content seem to be related over widely separated areas on the globe.

> The countries at the eastern end of the Mediterranean Sea were exchanging musical ideas and instruments with Greece at least 5,000 years ago. The desire for trade carried men by land and by sea from that part of the world to places as far west as England and Ireland, as far east as India and China. In their travels they spread customs and habits so widely that it is difficult now to decide which country was the first to have them. The aulos, a pipe with double reeds like an oboe and with the piercing sound of a bagpipe, was a favorite Greek instrument. It is, however, almost exactly like pipes found in the Orient, on the island of Java, and in the South American countries of Bolivia and Peru. Its shrill, disturbing music was sometimes used for war, sometimes for wild dances and celebrations. The Scottish and Irish bagpipes were forms of the aulos.[39]

---

[39]Urana Clarke, "How Our Music Began" *The Book of Knowledge* (Volume 18) New York, 1957, p. 6697

So many similarities of music over areas remote from one another seem to be more than can be explained as chance or just coincidence. Instead, the evidence is strong for cultural interaction of people who were geographically widely separated. A case in point is the use of musical scales. Musical scales are very specific even to the point of exact mathematical relationships between vibration frequencies of the various notes of a scale. Scales are also very ancient. In fact, the scales that we use today are the same as those used in China over four thousand years ago. Much later the Greeks used the same scales. These scales were also used by Indians in western North America.

> It is interesting to find that among the western Canadian Indians from the province of British Columbia there are songs that use a Greek scale like the one on the white keys going down from e. It is possible that courageous explorers set sail from China in an effort to cross the Pacific long before the birth of Christ. The merchants of that country used ships called junks that were far more seaworthy than the Pinta, Niña and Santa Maria in which Columbus crossed the Atlantic 2,000 years later. Chinese junks are gaily decorated and all of them have eyes painted on each side of the bow, to help the ship find its way through dangerous waters. British Columbian Indians paint eyes on their canoes; they use Greek and Chinese scales and follow other customs like those of the Chinese.[40]

In Central America also there is evidence of very ancient cultural and "racial" contact between peoples

[40]Urana Clarke, p. 6698

from widely separated areas of the globe. One item of evidence is the large stone heads found in Central America. These heads are very accurately carved from hard basalt rock. Physical features and even facial expressions are clearly evident. In fact, details are so accurately sculptured as to even suggest that actual individuals were used as models. Some of these heads have been unearthed in eastern Mexico along the Gulf of Mexico.

> All were monoliths carved out of basalt and similarly durable materials. Some took the form of gigantic heads weighing up to thirty tons. Others were massive stelae engraved with encounter scenes apparently involving two distinct races of mankind, neither of them American-Indian. Whoever had produced these outstanding works of art had obviously belonged to a refined, well organized, prosperous and technologically advanced civilization.[41]

Commenting on an archaeological find near the town of Santiago Tuxtla, Hancock comments,

> A leafy little park occupied the centre of this square, and in the centre of the park, like some magic talisman, stood an enormous grey boulder, almost ten feet tall, carved in the shape of a helmeted African head. Full-lipped and strong-nosed, its eyes serenely closed and its lower jaw resting squarely on the ground, this head had a sombre and patient gravity. Here, then, was the first mystery of the Olmecs: a monumental piece of sculpture, more than 2000 years old, which portrayed a subject with unmistakable negroid features. There were, of course, no African blacks in the

---

[41]Graham Hancock, *Fingerprints of the Gods*, New York, Crown Trade Paperbacks, 1995, p. 120

New World 2000 years ago, nor did any arrive until the slave trade began, well after the conquest. There is, however, firm palaeoanthropological evidence that one of the many different migrations into the Americas during the last Ice Age *did* consist of people of negroid stock.[42]

Archaeologists have also uncovered sculptures of individuals showing startlingly clear Caucasian features in Mexico.

> Matthew Stirling, the American archaeologist who excavated La Venta (Mexico) in the 1940s, made a number of spectacular discoveries there. The most spectacular of all was the Stele of the Bearded Man. ... It so obviously depicted a Caucasian male with a high-bridged nose and a long, flowing beard that the bemused archaeologists promptly christened it 'Uncle Sam'. ... And, as was the case with the negro heads, it was obvious that the face of the bearded Caucasian man could only have been sculpted from a human model. The racial verisimilitude was too good for an artist to have invented it.[43]

Taken together these evidences strongly support the idea that there was in fact cross-cultural and racial contact between people from widely separated geographical areas of the globe. We will have more to say about the origin of the various "races" later in chapter nine. In each geographically diverse and separated location, there is evidence, too, of advanced technology. Also there is no indication at all of the technology slowly being devel-

---

[42]Hancock, p. 120-121

[43]Hancock, p. 132-133

oped. It was there at each location from the very beginning. What events in world history could account for these puzzles? A foundation for answering these and similar questions is provided by the Biblical outline of history.

Stone heads similar to the one above have been discovered in various places in Mexico and are believed to be about four thousand years old. Facial features show definite negroid characteristics. Features are so clear and characteristic as to strongly suggest that an actual human was used as a model. Artifacts depicting other racial features have also been discovered. The figurine on the right clearly shows Oriental characteristics.

Photos by Helen Culp

After the Flood, the entire earth was carefully surveyed as mentioned in the previous chapter. In Peleg's days after the Flood the descendants of Noah appear to have surveyed, mapped, and explored the entire post-flood world. Necessary technological requirements for accomplishing this task such as surveying instruments, advanced knowledge of navigation and mathematics were available to these rebuilders of civilization after the Flood. They either utilized knowledge which had been developed before the Flood, or they built on and rapidly developed further, that pre-Flood knowledge. They continued to make new discoveries and invent new technology. No doubt one of their reasons for surveying the entire world was to locate sources for strategic materials. These materials would have been needed for rebuilding a civilization incorporating advanced technology and to make even further progress with new technology.

In addition to these finds archaeological evidence indicates that Egyptians and Orientals may also have been involved with commerce to Central America. Items have been found which clearly show physical features associated with Egyptians and with Asians.

Post-Flood bronze

Archaeological results have revealed the use of advanced metallurgy in early Mesopotamia. Iron and other metals were used. As already mentioned in Chapter three, early post-Flood civilization worked with the metal alloy bronze (an alloy of copper and tin). Archaeology has also shown that bronze was an important item to Babylonian civilization. Although copper is mined in the area of the Middle East, very little, if any, tin is available.

It must have been obtained elsewhere in such places as the British Isles, the Great Lakes region of North America and perhaps the high Andes Mountains of South America, e.g. Bolivia. Early post-Flood dwellers of Mesopotamia must thus have been able to navigate ships to these areas to carry on such commerce. Considerable evidence now lends support to that idea.

Ancient Maps

An increasingly large amount of evidence indicates that early post-Flood dwellers possessed an amazing amount of accurate knowledge of the globe.[44]

> It is very apparent from the generation list of the sons of Noah that the post-Flood peoples spread rapidly across the surface of the earth. ... It also becomes obvious that in order for the Genesis 10 genealogy list to have been composed, there must have been an advanced degree of communication among all these people. Someone living during the colonizing of these distant lands had the ability to correspond with all the descendants over a relatively long period of time — otherwise the composition of such a detailed listing as the 'Table of Nations' would have been impossible. This communication between remote regions presupposes an early knowledge of geography. In fact, there is ample evidence that not long after the Deluge, the descendants of Noah carried out an extensive survey of the entire globe, mapping and charting every continent![45]

---

[44]Graham Hancock, *Fingerprints of the Gods*, New York, Crown Trade Paperbacks, 1995

[45]Rene Noorbergen, *Secrets of the Lost Races*, Norcom Publishing: Collegedale, TN, 1992, p. 94

Noorbergen indicates that there must have been "an advanced degree of communication" among people in widely separated geographical areas. Rather than having only an occasional contact with each other every few centuries or so, traders made regular visits in order to carry on commerce. A few individuals thus probably had the ability to speak several languages and to carry news back and forth.

In the evolutionary model it is commonly assumed that early peoples were "primitive" and that they therefore were not only incapable of navigating and sailing the seas to remote regions, but that they were ignorant of those remote regions as well. However, such an arrogant assumption does not agree with archaeological facts.

Copies of very ancient maps such as the Piri Reis Map show that the ancients not only were aware of world geography, but that they accurately mapped it as well. For example, the entire coastline of Antarctica before the ice age was mapped including the location of the south geographic pole.[46] Because the ice age began soon after the Flood,[47] the mapping must have been carried out very early during post-Flood times. This is in agreement with the time when Peleg was alive according to genealogical records. It is in agreement with the concept stated in Genesis 10:25 as discussed earlier in chapter four.

It is not surprising, therefore, to learn that the very early inhabitants of South America at such locations as Sacsahuaman and Tiahuanaco not only were highly capable technologically, but also had contact with various

---

[46]Charles Hapgood, *Maps of the Ancient Sea Kings: Evidence of Advanced Civilization in the Ice Age*, Philadelphia, Chilton Books, 1966

[47]Michael J. Oard, *An Ice Age Caused by the Genesis Flood*, San Diego, Institute for Creation Research, 1990

racial types. As already mentioned in chapter one, Thor Heyerdahl of Kon Tiki fame "wonders whether civilization did indeed peak long, long ago."[48] Thor Heyerdahl, contrary to established modern views, believed that early

Present-day Indians living on Lake Titicaca fabricate reed boats strikingly similar in construction and in shape to those used along the Nile River in Ancient Egypt.

Photo by David Hooley

Egyptian influence in the ancient western hemisphere is also evident from this figurine discovered in Mexico.

Photo by Helen Culp

[48]Thomas Moore, "Thor Heyerdahl: Sailing Against the Current" *U.S. News & World Report*, April 2, 1990, p. 60.

people did possess both the knowledge and technical capability to navigate between the Old World and the New World. He staked his life on that belief by proving that intercontinental sea voyages were possible in even a "primitive" boat constructed of reeds.[49]

The puzzle pieces are starting to fit together to reveal the whole picture.

---

[49] Thor Heyerdahl, *Aku Aku: the secret of Easter Island*, Chicago: Rand McNally, 1958 and *Kon Tiki: across the Pacific by raft*, Chicago: Rand McNally, 1950.

CHAPTER VI

THE TOWER OF BABEL

C ontinuing now in Genesis 11, "And it came to
pass as they journeyed from the east, that they
found a plain in the land of Shinar and they
dwelt there. And they said one to another, 'Go to, let us
make brick and burn them thoroughly.' And they had
brick for stone and slime they had for mortar. And they
said, 'Go to, let us build us a city and a tower whose top
may reach unto heaven, and let us make us a name, lest
we be scattered abroad upon the face of the earth.'" Thus
they began to build the Tower of Babel. What was the
motive for building the tower of Babel? Ask the average
person who has even a cursory knowledge of the Bible
and he'll tell you, "Oh they were trying to get up to be
where God is." That's not what the Bible says. The Bible
says "lest we be scattered." (Genesis 11:4) One of the
motivations involved with building the tower of Babel
was to prevent themselves from being scattered. Yet God
had commanded them to scatter.[50] Man's response was,
"We're not going to do it." Perhaps Nimrod was a shrewd
enough dictator to realize that if the people scattered all
over the earth, he wouldn't have anybody to dictate to.
His goal of being ruler of a world empire would be
hindered so he arranged for a big public works project to
build the tower of Babel.

They were building a tower "whose top may reach

---

[50] Genesis 9:1

unto heaven." At first glance this phrase might give one the impression that they were planning on building a very, very tall tower. Some have even suggested that the phrase meant a tower tall enough to get up to where God dwelled or to escape being drowned in case of another flood. However, a bit of thought reveals that it would not be possible to stack bricks to extreme heights. Bricks would either be crushed under the burden of their own weight or the tower would fall over. If the builders of the tower of Babel were as technically advanced as archaeology shows us they were, they would most certainly have been aware of the limitations of bricks. No, a closer examination of the phrase "whose top may reach unto heaven" shows that the phrase has a meaning similar to what we use when we say that a bigger telescope is being built, one which will reach further out into space. When that phrase is used, do we mean that our telescope will reach out and physically touch the stars? Of course we do not mean that. Instead, the phrase "reach out into space" means that we will observe and study the stars. In a similar manner the Tower of Babel was for the purpose of observing and studying astronomical objects. Why were they so intent on studying astronomical objects? Studies related to the Tower of Babel have shown the reason.[51] Under the leadership of Nimrod, the world's first dictator, the early post-Flood people rebelled against the Creator's command for them to scatter out and repopulate the earth. Already in a state of rebellion and in defiance of the Creator's command, they invented a counterfeit religious system known as astrology instead of worshipping the Creator. As is well known, astrology

[51]Rev. Alexander Hislop, *The Two Babylons*, Neptune NJ, Loizeaux Brothers, 1959

requires a knowledge of the positions and movements of astronomical objects.

Astrology is a counterfeit religion, and should not be confused with astronomy, which is a science. Astrology involves the twelve signs of the zodiac (Aquarius, Virgo, Taurus, Gemini, etc.). The beliefs of astrology are that motions of astronomical objects strongly influence, if not control, people's lives. Thus astrology has people using motions and positions of planets and stars to find out how to live and to guide their lives and the decisions they make, instead of going to the true Creator God.

Under Nimrod, people not only disobeyed God and refused to scatter as He had instructed them to, but they invented and practiced the counterfeit religion of astrology. It quickly degenerated to a vicious, degrading system. Archaeological research as well as historical records, including the Old Testament, reveal some of the sordid details. For example, human sacrifice was included, including forcing their own children to walk through fire until burned to death. These practices continued and increased among the inhabitants of the area known Biblically as Canaan. When the Israelites entered Canaan, the promised land, God repeatedly warned them not to practice those pagan and degrading rituals. "There shall not be found among you any one that maketh his son or his daughter to pass through the fire, or that useth divination, or an observer of times, or an enchanter, or a witch." (Deut. 18:10) "And they have built the high places of Tophet, which is in the valley of the son of Hinnom, to burn their sons and their daughters in the fire; which I commanded them not, neither came it into my heart." (Jer. 7:31) See also Lev. 18:21,

Deut 2:31, II Kings 16:3, 17:17, 21:6, II Chr. 28:3, 33:6, Ezek. 20:31. Under Nimrod, things were continuing to degenerate spiritually and morally.

Continuing now with Genesis 11:5-6,

> And the LORD came down to see the city and the tower, which the children of men builded. And the LORD said, Behold, the people is one, and they have all one language: and this they begin to do: and now nothing will be restrained from them, which they have imagined to do.

If the people could conceive, or think of, or imagine some technological achievement or application, they would probably be able to carry it out or soon would be able to, considering their rapidly advancing technology. Even though because of the Fall man had been degenerating, they were still, in all likelihood, far more capable than we are today. They were closer to creation and had not degenerated physically and intellectually as far as we have. In addition they had no language barriers to prevent communication and mutual cooperation. Rapid technological progress was not hindered as it is today by language barriers. And since poor communication between people groups many times leads to war, speaking the same language would have allowed them to devote their full energies to technological progress rather than military campaigns.

Also, average lifetimes were considerably greater than for people living today. Therefore, with these advantages, and also from inheriting a base of high technology from before the Flood, people under Nimrod could achieve amazing technological feats in a relatively short time. If they could "imagine to do" it, they could probably accomplish the doing of it.

Yet even with all the potential for the betterment of civilization, there is a sad note to their accomplishments. The Scriptures tell us that man has a natural bent toward evil (Jer. 17:9, Ecc. 8:11). By having a bent toward evil and assisted technologically, man in rebellion against his Creator can turn his habitat into a living Hell. I was born before World War II and remember how technology was used to torture and murder and mutilate human beings. The Nazis in Germany performed horrible "scientific" experiments on people. Philosophical justification for these atrocities came from their naturalistic, atheistic view of origins.

Before a technological advancement can occur, it first must be envisioned. In the late years of the 1930's, I remember reading an article in a popular semi-technical magazine, perhaps *Popular Mechanics* or some similar magazine. At that time, experiments were just beginning with liquid-fueled rockets. On the cover of the magazine was an artist's rendition of an advanced rocket on its way into space. The article inside stated that a liquid-fueled rocket had been built which could attain an altitude of one hundred thousand *feet*. While that was a highly significant achievement at the time, the article further stated that the eventual goal was to develop a rocket with the capability of taking men to the moon and returning. I was extremely fascinated and excited about that possibility. However, when I told my mother about it, she laughed at the idea. She said, "Going to the moon is such an impossible technological task that it will never be carried out!" Yet I have lived to see that actually happen.

Even my mother lived to see it. Men have actually traveled to the moon, walked on its surface, and returned to earth. It all began when some visionaries in the field of technology imagined that man would walk on the moon. That imagining eventually in a few decades became a reality, even within my lifetime.

Nowadays we speak of other imaginative ideas such as test tube babies, genetic engineering and computer control of society. If patterns of past similar situations hold true for these present-day imaginings, such technological applications may also become reality. But man in rebellion against the Creator can use technology to manipulate and destroy other human beings. By wrong application, technology can indeed be used to turn the world into a living Hell.

However, the Creator restrains and judges evil. Even in His judgments, though, the Creator is gracious. The evil direction and developments taken by early post-Flood mankind under Nimrod would be checked. "Go to, let us go down, and there confound their language, that they may not understand one another's speech. So the LORD scattered them abroad from thence upon the face of all the earth: and they left off to build the city." (Genesis 11:7-9)

Modern studies on the origins of languages lend support to the confusion of tongues at Babel.

> Linguistics ... compares related languages to reconstruct their immediate progenitors and eventually their ultimate ancestor, or protolanguage. ... The science developed from the study of the Indo-European superfamily of languages, by far the largest in number of languages and number of speakers. Nearly

half of the world's population speaks an Indo-European language as a first language...[52]

Where is the geographical location from which these other languages radiated?

> The landscape described by the protolanguage as now resolved must be somewhere in the crescent that curves around the southern shores of the Black Sea, south from the Balkan peninsula, east across ancient Anatolia (today the non-European territories of Turkey) and north to the Caucasus Mountains.[53]

Available evidence thus lends support to the confusion of languages at the Tower of Babel

The Creator's intent for man was for him to disperse out over the globe after the Flood. But because man rebelled and refused to disperse, the Creator brought forth judgment by confounding their language. Because people could no longer easily and naturally communicate, social isolation occurred. Small groups, limited perhaps to families or tribes each speaking its own unique tongue, then naturally developed a "we" versus "they" mentality. Each group vied for available land and other resources, resulting in further isolation both socially and politically. Genesis chapter ten lists the various groups and locations where they migrated and settled. The ability of all mankind to speak a common language had the potential to have been a tremendous blessing. It was lost because of man's sin and rebellion against the Creator.

---

[52]Thomas V. Gamkrelidze and V. V. Ivanov, "The Early History of Indo-European Languages" *Scientific American*, March 1990, p. 110.

[53]Gamkrelidze & Ivanov, "The Early History of Indo-European Languages" *Scientific American*, March 1990, pp. 111-112.

The Creator's intent that man disperse was accomplished, as His intents eventually always will be. However, man can save himself a lot of difficulty and trouble by responding voluntarily to carrying out the Lord's will instead of being forced by judgment to do so. What was the result of confusion of languages on subsequent history? Do the pyramids and other artifacts from the ancient past have a story to tell?

CHAPTER VII

MEGALITH PUZZLE PIECES

The last chapter provided an overview of early post-Flood events. We saw that Nimrod, the great-grandson of Noah, became the first world dictator. Under Nimrod not only was there a high technology developed, but also a counterfeit religious system associated with astrology. However, their rebellion against the Creator's command to disperse and to re-populate the post-Flood earth, as well as the counterfeit religious system they developed and practiced, eventually brought on judgment by the Creator. He confused their languages and then people dispersed out from Babel. In summary, the Biblical picture is one of a centralized, technically advanced civilization which quickly dispersed away from the Middle East.

In this chapter, as we examine some archaeological evidence, we shall find that it supports this picture of early post-Flood civilization. Such a large amount of evidence is already in existence, with more being discovered all the time, that a full discussion of it would require more space than is our purpose here. Therefore only several representative lines and major items of evidence will be discussed, showing an outline or summary of historical developments since Babel. For a more complete discussion, the reader may consult items listed in the Bibliography. The author hopes the representative

samples of evidence that are presented will be sufficient
for the reader to readily discern an overall general pattern. Then after discerning the general pattern, the reader
will find it to match the Biblical picture.

Ziggurats

In the Middle East, archaeologists discovered features
which at first glance appeared to be merely piles of dirt
situated in unlikely locations. Viewed from the air,
however, they appeared in a larger context and significant
details showed up which were not readily discernible
from the ground. From the air it was apparent that what
at first appearance seemed just piles of dirt were, in fact,
the remains of man-made objects. Upon further examination of these objects, it was discovered that they were
the remains of edifices known as ziggurats. Ziggurats
were the original pyramids and were carefully constructed, carefully engineered, and of high quality. It is
now known that they were used for religious purposes
and also were associated with astrology.[54] Inscriptions
and other evidence show the astrological significance of
the ziggurats. Apparently the peoples associated with
them worshipped the sun, moon, planets and stars rather
than the Creator.

Worship of any but the true God always leads to
cultural and moral degeneration. History confirms such a
pattern and result over and over again. As Proverbs 14:34
states, "Righteousness exalteth a nation, but sin is a
reproach to any people." Again we read, "The wages of
sin is death, but the gift of God is eternal life through

---

[54]Roman Ghirshman, "The Ziggurat of Tchoga-Zanbil" *Scientific American*,
January 1961, pp. 69-76.

Jesus Christ our Lord." Sin (rebellion against the Creator) leads to death. This is true for a culture as well as an individual. An example is the region where ziggurats once were prominent. All that remains today are the findings of scientists, half-buried ruins, and the mounds of once-towering ziggurats, still rising above the silent, hot Iraqi desert. That once great culture with all of its surprisingly high technology is now dead. All that remains are ruins.

Those who migrated away from Babel after the confusion of languages carried much of Babel's culture with them. Probably not all features or all aspects of the technology were re-established by each family or group in its new location. Even though the knowledge of the existence of the technology may have been present with each migrating group, all the skills and resources necessary for implementing it likely were not. General features, however, were retained and used in each new environment, especially the religious aspects. An examination of historical records and data from archaeology support this idea.

Egypt

Chapter ten of Genesis provides a detailed account of the scattering out from Babel, and of the nations which eventually developed from those scattered. Some scattered to the area which became known as Egypt. Although they scattered as did other groups, they carried with them the pagan and counterfeit religion of Nimrod. The early Egyptians immediately began to build pyramids. As is well known, one of the big puzzles for secular (non-Biblical) archaeology has been the origin of

One of the puzzles concerning Ancient Egyptian pyramids is the high quality of the first ones. It is a puzzle because there has been no evidence whatsoever of any experimentation to learn how to build pyramids. Later pyramids were of inferior quality.

Photos by Seth Wilson

the Egyptian pyramids.[55] They are technically sophisticated structures. Yet no evidence has been discovered of experimentation leading up to pyramid building.

> (T)here is no evidence whatever of any technological breakthrough in the methods of quarrying or cutting stone which might account for the onset of pyramid building. All the tools and techniques used by the pyramid builders were in existence well before their time.[56]

[55]Graham Hancock, *Fingerprints of the Gods*, New York, Crown Trade Paperbacks, 1995, p. 135-136.

[56]Kurt Mendelssohn, "A Scientist Looks at the Pyramids" *American Scientist*, 1971 March-April, p. 210.

The archaeological evidence suggested that rather than developing slowly and painfully, as is normal with human societies, the civilization of Ancient Egypt, like that of the Olmecs, emerged *all at once and fully formed*. Indeed, the period of transition from primitive to advanced society appears to have been so short that it makes no kind of historical sense. Technological skills that should have taken hundreds or even thousands of years to evolve were brought into use almost overnight — and with no apparent antecedents whatever.[57] (emphasis his)

There seems to be no evidence to show how the technology needed for pyramid building was acquired or developed. How did the required technology arise? Again Hancock comments, "What is remarkable is that there are no traces of evolution from simple to sophisticated, and the same is true of mathematics, medicine, astronomy and architecture and of Egypt's amazingly rich and convoluted religio-mythological system..."[58] The first and earliest pyramids are the best. Later ones were inferior copies. Quality continued to decline until pyramids eventually were no longer built.

The pyramid age had come to an end, having lasted for a little more than a century. Pyramids were still being erected for about a thousand years, but they rapidly became smaller and shoddier, and it is quite clear that with the third Giza pyramid the zest had gone out of pyramid building forever.[59]

---

[57]Hancock, p. 135

[58]Hancock, p. 135

[59]Mendelssohn, p. 212.

The early pyramids were of exceedingly high quality both mathematically and architecturally. Even today with our supposedly high modern technology, we do not know or understand how the pyramids were built. There has been seemingly no end of ideas and speculations[60] as to how the pyramids were built, but no one really knows for certain.

Those who have studied the pyramids also note that they were very precisely aligned with astronomical objects. The pyramids had astrological significance just as did the ziggurats. From the Biblical perspective, however, such evidence is not surprising because those who founded Egypt traced their roots to Babel and the kingdom of Nimrod. The founders would have retained from Babel much of its culture, including its technology. Thus there was no need to experiment and develop technology used for building pyramids. When Scripture is taken seriously, as giving an actual and true account of history, the puzzle of sudden origin of Egyptian pyramids vanishes. Archaeological reality is seen to be in agreement with the Bible.

Minoan Civilization

While some scattered out from Babel to Egypt, others scattered westward to the Mediterranean and established the Minoan civilization, which was also a civilization with a high technology. Surviving historical accounts and documents claim that the Minoan civilization had knowledge of such items as electric batteries and sophisticated mechanical or gear-type

---

[60]Dr. Joseph Davidovits, Margie Morris, *The Pyramids: An Enigma Solved*, New York, Dorset Press, 1990

computing devices, or computers. Because of the commonly-held modern assumption that ancient people were "primitive," these accounts of an early and high technology were disbelieved and relegated to the status of myth or legend.

Recent investigations, however, have shown that these accounts of early high technology were not myths, but reliable historical records. The Minoans did have access to electric batteries and to computing devices. Ancient batteries used copper and iron as electrodes in place of carbon and zinc as is common in many modern batteries. However copper and iron are materials which, it is now known, can function quite adequately as electrodes for a battery.

Wilhelm König, director of the Baghdad Museum and Iraq Antiquities Department, reported in 1938 the discovery of electric batteries in an area near Baghdad. For various reasons exact dating of the batteries is difficult, but reported dates range from about 100 B.C. to 100 A.D. What was the purpose of the batteries? How were they used? We do not know the answer to these questions, but several suggestions have been made. Suggestions range from their use for electroplating to usage in medical practice as a local electrical analgesic. If the dating of these objects is even approximately correct, then it is possible that they may be degenerated copies of earlier, more advanced versions. Batteries may have suffered a fate similar to that of the pyramids. In the case of Egyptian pyramids, the first ones were the best. Later pyramids became increasingly more shoddy until eventually they were no longer built. The same may apply to electric batteries. As one researcher on these ancient batteries comments, "It is probable that the device later became merely a conjurer's trick and gradually faded from view, just as the magicians of Mesopotamia did."[61]

What about the legends of supposed ancient computing devices? Two types of computing devices are in use in modern culture, analog computers and digital computers. Analog computers indicate their answers, or output, by means of dials in a manner similar to the hands on an ordinary clock. Digital computers on the other hand, indicate their output with numerals as on a digital clock. A surprisingly sophisticated analog computing device was recovered from a ship which sank in the Aegean Sea more than two thousand years ago.[62] When first recovered, the analog computer was covered with mud and somewhat corroded. However when it had been cleaned up and studied by modern techniques such as auto-radiography, the device revealed an amazing amount of technical design and capability. It was a finely crafted mechanical device and even contained differential gears. We did not rediscover how to make differential gears until modern times. One of the things it was apparently used for was navigation and for accurately calculating the position of a ship while sailing the seas. Such accurate navigating techniques were not rediscovered until relatively recent times.

Concerning the early Mediterranean civilization we have from the Odyssey of Homer, "There is a land called Crete in the midst of the wine-dark sea, ...and therein are many men, past counting, and ninety cities ... among

[61]Paul T. Keyser, "The Purpose of the Parthian Galvanic Cells: A First-Century A.D. Electric Battery Used for Analgesia" *Journal of Near Eastern Studies*, 52 no. 2 (1993), p. 98.

[62]"The Seminal Science" *Mosaic* May/June 1978, pp. 2-8

them is the great city Knossos where Minos reigned, ... he that held converse with great Zeus ..."[63] Again we observe the close association this civilization had with astronomical objects and astrology. The Minoans also trace their roots back to Nimrod's kingdom.

Stonehenge

Still others scattered from the Babel area to the British Isles. Do we observe there also an association with Nimrod's kingdom, as in Egypt and the Mediterranean? Indeed we do! In the British Isles there are many henges, large stones that are set in a circular arrangement with astronomical alignments and astrological usage. They are associated with the Druids and their religious rituals. Perhaps the most famous of these henges is Stonehenge located on the Salisbury Plain. These stones are not of local origin, but were quarried over seventy-five miles away and then moved into place. Some of the stones are also quite large, weighing in excess of an estimated one hundred tons! A stone that large will depress the ground upon which it is placed. Yet these stones were accurately placed so that they would be in exact astronomical alignment. In fact the alignment was so precise that it was not until 1962, by using a modern digital computer at Massachusetts Institute of Technology, that we discovered the exactness of the alignment and some of the purposes and uses of Stonehenge.[64] Yet the builders of

---

[63]Homer, *The Odyssey*, Book 19 (The Harvard Classics, edited by Charles W. Eliot LL.D., Translated by S.H. Butcher & A. Lang), P.F. Collier & Son New York (1909), p. 272.

[64] Gerald S. Hawkins, "Sun, Moon, Men, and Stones" *American Scientist*, December 1965 (Vol. 53, No. 4), pp. 391-408. See also Patrick Moore "The Oldest Science in the World" *Science Digest*, October 1962, pp. 15-20 and "Stones of Time" *Newsweek*, November 18, 1963, p. 103.

Even with modern studies of Stonehenge, it is still a mystery as to exactly how its builders moved these large stones from their source a considerable distance away, and then positioned them so accurately.

Stonehenge appears to be an extremely accurate astronomical calculator.

Photos by Steve and Carla Allemann

Stonehenge had somehow already calculated how much the earth would be depressed when a large stone was placed upon it, so that the massive stones, when put in place, would still be perfectly aligned astronomically. It is difficult to believe that the builders of Stonehenge were "primitive" people when they obviously possessed the technical skill required for Stonehenge. It is much more reasonable to believe that they utilized skills already possessed and developed earlier at Babel.

Zimbabwe

Continuing now with a description of areas where people established cultures after dispersal from Babel, we again encounter evidence of advanced technology in Africa. One such example is the Zimbabwe Ruins in what formerly was called Rhodesia. The walls and other

Stone structures at Zimbabwe are constructed without mortar. That fact requires that individual stones mesh together accurately.

The tower theme at Zimbabwe is reminiscent of an earlier tower theme at Babel. Photographs by Mrs. DeMille

structures of these ruins are made of stone. An examination of a wall shows it to be constructed of stones several inches in cross section with each stone about six <u>feet</u> in length. So well fitted are the stones that no mortar was required to hold the structure together. Yet the wall and other structures have stood these many, many years. It is also interesting to observe again at Zimbabwe a prominent tower structure apparently associated with astrology. This observation is not surprising in view of the Biblical picture of a dispersion from Babel and their association with astrology.

If a technically advanced culture was developed in the Middle East and was dispersed out from that area, how then does cave man fit in? Cave man, or Neanderthal as he is more accurately known, is supposed to have been primitive man possessing only a primitive culture and tools. He is popularly pictured with stooped posture, carrying a club and dragging a woman by her hair. How accurate is this picture?

CHAPTER VIII

CAVE MAN

At this point we shall pause in our discussion of archaeological evidences and seek to answer two common questions which arise in discussions on the origin of man. The first question is "How does 'cave man' fit in?" A second question concerns an explanation for the origin of the "races." This chapter will examine the question of cave man and the next chapter, the question of the origin of "races."

In answering these questions, a diagram is helpful. Under Nimrod's rule the people located in and around the Tower of Babel, rebuilt, and probably developed even further, the advanced technology from before the Flood. However, the confounding of language caused a rapid scattering out from the Middle East to new and unsettled areas. Finding themselves thus in a new and unfamiliar environment, the small bands or families which dispersed out from Babel needed time to study each new environment and to adjust to it. Climates and other features would be different. It was perhaps also necessary to learn to raise and harvest new crops for food and other uses. Fruit orchards, vineyards, and the like would require considerable time to be planted and mature to the point of being productive. For those who may have migrated to tropical regions, there would have been additional problems of poisonous snakes, insects, and plants, etc.

For these reasons, considerable time and effort would be invested in just surviving in the new environment.

Little or no extra time would have been available for building or developing an advanced technology even though they may have known of its possibilities from their memories of Babel. As a consequence, the first wave of migrants out from the Middle East would experience culture loss. Also, under these stressful conditions, it was not possible for them to develop any significant military defenses involving the use of advanced technology. Such development was greatly hindered or even impossible. Each group had only a small population base. Surplus manpower above that needed for obtaining basic necessities of living was simply not available until considerable time had passed. Time would be required for the population to increase and provide the necessary manpower. About all they would have been able to produce militarily would have been a few "primitive" defensive instruments such as spears or perhaps bows and arrows. Yet those who remained behind at Babel still retained their technical advantages. It is perhaps predictable what was to happen subsequently.

Those possessing technological advantage eventually yielded to the temptation to take advantage of those less capable. Raids were conducted on those who had migrated out from Babel. Perhaps some were even taken captive and returned as slaves to the Middle East. Thus, in an effort to protect themselves and to hide, those with less technical capability rapidly migrated to even more remote areas. Of particular interest to us are those who migrated to what is now known as northern and western Europe.

Those migrants faced additional challenges. In this geographical area, climate and living conditions were

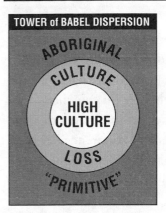

Figure 2: At the dispersion of peoples out from the area of the Tower of Babel, the first wave of migrants suffered culture loss. These peripheral cultures would today be termed "primitive" when in actuality they were anything but primitive, and should be viewed as de-cultured.

harsh because of the advancing Ice Age at that time.[65] In order to cope with the harsh weather, caves were utilized as shelters and living quarters. These early settlers at the edge of the ice were "cave men." May I suggest therefore that "cave man" was not primitive man, but rather, cave man was de-cultured man. They (the cave dwellers) were intellectually quite capable, but had suffered cultural loss and would incorrectly be termed aboriginal or primitive by those who believe that man had evolved up from an animal.

However, newer studies, even by those who believe that man evolved, have shown that Neanderthal man and Cro-Magnon man were not primitive.

> For years, many anthropologists have maintained that Neanderthal man disappeared from Earth approximately 35,000 years ago. 'But the fact is, the West European Neanderthals are today's West Europeans,' says C. Loring Brace, curator of the physical anthropology division at the University of Michigan's

---

[65]Michael Oard, *An Ice Age Caused By The Genesis Flood*, San Diego, Institute for Creation Research, 1990

Museum of Anthropology. ... 'In every respect, the shape of the modern West European skull is closer to the shape of the classic Neanderthal cranium than to that of any other modern group in other parts of the world,' he says, adding that there is no evidence Neanderthals walked any less erect than modern man and from the neck down, the only difference between Neanderthals and modern man is the 'indication of generally greater ruggedness in Neanderthal joints and muscles.'[66]

Both Neanderthal and Cro-Magnon possessed larger brain capacities, on the average, than modern man. The evolutionary explanation for man's origin teaches that as man evolved up from the animal, his brain was evolving and becoming larger. Thus, using the evolutionary scenario and judging only from brain size, cave man would have been smarter than modern man! Again, using only brain size as a criterion, it appears that man has been degenerating since cave man times because our brain sizes now (judging by cranial capacity) are smaller than cave man's. In any case, actual evidence indicates cave man to have been quite capable intellectually. Some hint of their excellent mental capabilities can be gleaned from their cave art. Cave art is anything but primitive. Drawings of animals, for example, were of lifelike quality. Some drawings were even so cleverly crafted as to provide a three-dimensional effect. Modern artists would be challenged to do as well.

It has also been discovered that some of the unusual physical features (so-called primitive features, such as

---

[66]John Holmes, "Neanderthals Linked to West Europeans" *Insight* September 11, 1989, p. 56

bone shapes or stooped posture, for instance) were the direct result of bone diseases. Deficiency in vitamin D is an example. Lack of vitamin D results in a bone disease known as rickets. Cave men were deficient in vitamin D primarily because of the lack of sunshine. Sunshine on the skin produces vitamin D and sunny weather was only minimally available. Because of the advancing ice during the ice age, weather conditions produced a much more cloudy and rainy climate, thus reducing the amount of sunshine.

How else did sunshine affect the migrating human population? Did it have anything to do with the origin of the "races"?

THE ORIGIN OF "RACES"

A second common question concerning the origin of man is the question of where the various races originated. Strictly speaking in the scientific and in the Biblical[67] sense, there really is no such thing as race. We are all members of only one race: the human race. All human beings can intermarry and produce children regardless of "race" and are accordingly, in the scientific sense, members of the same biological species. In addition, the Scriptures make no reference to race whatsoever. Physical features which are usually associated with race, such as round or slanted eyes, hair texture and skin color are not mentioned.

One possible exception to the Bible's speaking of skin color is its mention in a few places. "Can the Ethiopian change his skin, or the leopard his spots? Then may ye also do good, that are accustomed to do evil."[68]

> I am black, but comely, O ye daughters of Jerusalem, as the tents of Kedar, as the curtains of Solomon. Look not upon me, because I am black, because the sun hath looked upon me: my mother's children were angry with me; they made me the keeper of the vineyards; but mine own vineyard have I not kept.[69]

The first reference does not specifically single out any

[67]Acts 17:26

[68]Jeremiah 13:23

[69]Song of Solomon 1:5-6

particular feature of the skin, leaving open the option that it may possibly be color, but it is difficult to be dogmatic at this point. The second reference mentions skin color as black but seems to associate the dark color with long exposure to sunlight while working outdoors in the vineyards. It cannot be concluded from the passage that the color is genetically inherited and that it must therefore be a racial feature. Sociologists and cultural usage do, however, refer to race, and so we shall discuss that point briefly.

While in the strict sense there is no such thing as race, either scientifically or Biblically, it is nevertheless true that people in certain ethnic or geographic regions posses a predominance of certain physical features. Examples are Caucasian round eyes, or slant eyes associated with Orientals, or dark skin color for those with African roots. What is the origin of these special features if all people started with Adam and Eve? During my seminars on creation, a frequently asked question from a largely Caucasian audience is, "Where did black people come from?" Of course the unspoken assumption behind the question is that Adam and Eve were white and therefore black color must have originated somewhere somehow subsequent to creation. Such an assumption has absolutely no basis in fact and is indeed contrary to what is known about heredity.

The name Adam means "ruddy" or "red" which implies an intermediate shade. Native American Indians have a skin color which is middle brown. Early white settlers spoke of Indians as having red skin color.

The truth is that all human beings are of the same color! Everyone has the same chemical coloring agent, and it is the chemical melanin. Individuals whose genetic structure is such that they inherit the capability for their skin to produce very much melanin are "black." On the other hand, individuals inheriting the capability for their skin to produce very limited amounts of melanin are "white." Those who produce a moderate amount of melanin are middle "brown." Only people who are albinos have no melanin at all and their skin and hair are very light. Facts learned from the modern science of genetics fit very well with the Biblical view of creation and our origin from one common genetic source. For a more detailed discussion of race from a creationist view-point, one may refer to a discussion of that feature by three Australian authors who are scientists.[70]

Concerning the creation of mankind, the Scriptures simply state, "And the LORD God formed man of the dust of the ground, and breathed into his nostrils the breath of life, and man became a living soul." This verse brings to mind a somewhat humorous incident from the days when my wife and I were advisors for a church youth group. The occasion was a weekend retreat and the topic was on creation. After hearing the account of the creation of Adam and Eve, one particularly bright and alert ninth grade girl approached us where several of the group were discussing my presentation and asking questions. The girl's skin was very, very dark, almost black. She asked the question, "What color were Adam and Eve?" Before I could respond with a somewhat scientific answer, my wife, who is sometimes much quicker to size up situations, blurted out "dust-colored." The girl's

---

[70]Ken Ham, Andrew Snelling, and Carl Wieland, *The Answers Book*, Green Forest, AR: Master Books, 1990, pp. 131-155.

expression lightened up and a smile came across her face. She went away totally satisfied. It was a Scriptural answer and one that allowed for a person of any skin color to accept his color and also the Creation account. Adam was created "from the dust of the earth" and since dust of the earth comes in a variety of colors, "black" could have been one of them, and "white" or "brown" could have been also.

While it is true that there is much variation within a race, the fact remains that lighter skin characteristics are generally associated with people dwelling in cooler climates such as northern Europe. Darker-skinned peoples generally are native to geographical areas with hotter and sunnier climates. Why is this so?

An explanation is readily obtained by using the Biblical picture we have been discussing. Suppose that people who migrated out from the Middle East after the confusion of language at the tower of Babel were of middle brown skin color. With a middle brown population, some of the individuals would be darker, some lighter, as is the case with families from India or Arabia today. Initially individuals both with lighter and with darker skins would have been present in sunny and hot geographical areas such as Africa. The same would have been true for areas like Northern Europe with cloudier and cooler climates.

In hot areas with intense sunlight, people tend to wear fewer clothes because of the heat, thus exposing their skin to intense rays from the sun. Exposure to sunlight results not only in the production in the skin of vitamin D, a necessary item for healthy bones, but also in destructive photolysis of other vital substances such as folic acid. Loss of folic acid greatly reduces fertility. Also excessive sunlight penetrating the skin results in skin cancer. Dark skin with high pigmentation filters out much of the harmful rays from excessive sunlight. Dark skin allows just sufficient sunlight to enter the skin to synthesize enough vitamin D so the body remains healthy. Light skin on the other hand allows excessive amounts of the energetic rays from the sun to penetrate the skin, producing harmful effects. These harmful effects result in a greatly lowered fertility rate. People with light skin simply produced few children while people with dark skin retained high fertility. The net result would be that in a few generations only people with darker skin would be present in the population in areas with much sunlight.

In cloudier, cooler northern areas, the reverse process would occur. Light- and dark-skinned people were originally present in those areas with less sunshine. Because of the cooler climate, much of the body would be covered with clothes in order to keep warm. Because darker skin filters out sunlight and with much of the body covered by clothes, insufficient area of skin would be exposed to sunlight for production of healthy amounts of vitamin D. Lowered vitamin D results in the disease known as rickets, and other problems, and lowers the fertility rate. Light skin, in contrast, even with minimal surface exposed would be able to produce sufficient vitamin D for the body to remain healthy. Again, the net result would be that in a few generations, only lighter skinned people would be present in the colder cooler climates.

Although these same physiological factors, the need for vitamin D, sunlight's effects on skin, etc., are still operating now, most modern diets contain food items which contain vitamin D supplements. With adequate dietary vitamin D intake, people now seldom have a problem with obtaining a sufficient supply of the vitamin for good health.

Some scientific research seems to support the connection between skin pigmentation, fertility, exposure to sunlight, and geographic distribution.

> Deficiency of folate, which occurs in many marginally nour-ished populations, causes severe anemia, fetal wastage, frank infertility, and maternal mortality. Prevention of ultraviolet photolysis of folate and other light-sensitive nutrients by dark skin may be sufficient explanation for the maintenance of this characteristic in human groups indigenous to regions of intense solar radiation.[71]

As the size of the population grew in a geographically (and genetically) isolated group, certain features were accentuated and became predominant through intermarriage within the group. Individuals who dispersed out from the Tower of Babel possessed a wide variety of genetic traits. However no individual (or even family) possessed all genetic possibilities. After migrating out from Babel, groups settled in different areas and were somewhat geographically isolated. There was for each group a limited gene pool and intermarrying accentuated the traits of an isolated gene pool. These accentuated features are now associated with "race." However, as can be learned by observation, there can be as much or more difference between individuals within a so-called race as

---

[71]Richard F. Branda, John W. Eaton, "Skin Color and Nutrient Photolysis: An Evolutionary Hypothesis," *Science*, 18 August 1978, p. 625.

between races. For example, if one were to stand on a street corner in Japan and observe those passing by, wide variations could be observed. Some would have very light skin and some much more colored; some eyes would be very oriental and some almost Caucasian, etc.

"Race" is thus a sociological phenomenon rather than a Biblical or scientific one. It is used more out of convenience as a way of quickly classifying or stereotyping individuals and is not necessarily accurate. Instead, the important point to note is that there is only one race, the human "race." We all have a common origin, Creation. We all trace our roots to Adam and Eve.

As more puzzle pieces are examined and put into place, a picture is beginning to emerge. It shows a culture possessing technically advanced knowledge and located in the area of the Middle East at the dawn of human history. (Of course the real dawn of human history began before the Flood, a civilization largely lost to study, but secular history traces things back to the Middle East.) From there, elements of that culture and technology were suddenly seeded into Europe, Asia, and Africa. Did the Western Hemisphere also receive input of a similar nature?

THE NAZCA

Evidence of high technology from the distant past is by no means limited to the eastern hemisphere. Such evidence can be found also in South, Central, and North America. One such interesting example is located in the Nazca Desert south of Lima, Peru. It is famous for the lines, geometric figures and drawings of animals sketched on its surface. The Nazca Desert is one of the driest deserts in the world. Prevailing winds are from the east. As air from the east moves westward it is forced to rise as it crosses the high Andes mountains. As the air rises, it also cools and its moisture content condenses and precipitates out as rain or snow on the eastern slopes of the Andes. Once it is on the western side of the mountains, the air descends and warms. Thus, by the time it passes over the Nazca Desert, little or no moisture remains for precipitation. When my wife and I visited the Nazca Desert, we were told that the last time it had rained there was forty years earlier! A consequence of having no rain and also of only very mild, if any, surface wind is that there is essentially no erosion of the desert surface. As a consequence of extremely little moisture precipitation, the desert surface is not eroded by water. The designs and drawings also are not affected by desert breeze or covered by drifting sand.

It's true that high winds do blow here, but by a happy accident of physics they are robbed of their sting at ground level: the pebbles that litter the pampa absorb and retain the sun's heat, throwing up a protective force-field of warm air. In addition, the soil contains enough gypsum to glue small stones to the subsurface, an adhesive regularly renewed by the moistening effect of early morning dews. Once things [designs] are drawn here, therefore, they tend to stay drawn. There's hardly any rain; indeed, with less than half an hour of miserly drizzle every decade, Nazca is among the driest places on earth.[brackets mine][72]

Any ancient features on the desert surface remain largely undisturbed and are thus preserved.

The surface of the desert is also very, very flat. As one jokingly remarked, "It is so flat that it is necessary to put up a sign to tell the water which way to run." Lack of erosion and a flat surface are important points when considering one of the most interesting features of the Nazca Desert, namely the unusual markings and designs located there. Weather and wind have not disturbed them.

The markings on the surface of the Nazca Desert are straight lines, large geometric figures, and outlines of various animals. Because the desert is so very flat, the only really effective way of viewing these designs is from the air. In fact, a tower has been erected at one location so that visitors are able to obtain at least a limited view of some of the designs. However, the best method of viewing is from the air. When we visited the area in order to study the Nazca designs, we chartered an airplane for a forty-five minute flight over the desert.

The figures drawn on the desert are of various sizes and some are quite large. A few of the straight lines for example run as much as five miles and are perfectly

---

straight. In fact the lines are as straight as our best modern methods of aerial surveying could make them. On occasion, some of the lines will lead up to a small mountain or large mound only to proceed again on the other side for a great distance. Some appreciation of this accomplishment can be obtained when it is realized that these lines were constructed in spite of the flatness of the desert surface. It is apparent that fairly sophisticated instrumentation was needed for their construction.

> Regarding the methods employed, the designs of Nazca prove that their creators possessed a highly developed degree of abstract thought. The task of transferring to a desert the figure of a bird, or any other animal, is one that cannot be carried out by a mere enthusiast. It demands rather complicated geometric methods which alone can explain the extraordinary regularity and symmetry of the drawings as well as the proper proportions among their elements. It is quite certain that the figures of Nazca were not the result of a simple visual ad-hoc method.[73]

The Bonneville Salt Flats west of the Great Salt Lake in Utah can aid in an appreciation of the Nazcas' accomplishment. Because of its flatness and freedom from obstruction, the Bonneville Salt Flats are the location of the speedway for automotive world speed records. During a speed run, a vehicle starts its run and accelerates for a distance of five miles to reach its top speed at which point it is clocked. Then the vehicle has an additional five miles in which to decelerate and eventually stop. However an observer standing on one end of the raceway

---

[73]*Las lineas Nazca*, Lima, Perú, Librerías ABC S.A., 1978, p. 10.

cannot see the other end because of the curvature of the earth. The other end of the raceway has already fallen below the line of sight in a distance of just ten miles.

Traditional archaeologists have been quite puzzled by the markings in the Nazca desert. One of the causes for the puzzle is the flatness of the Nazca Desert and the curvature of the earth. The situation is similar to that with the Bonneville Salt Flats.

Thus, in order to construct the Nazca designs and especially the very straight lines, would require the capability to survey accurately. However, it is also commonly assumed that the ability to survey accurately is a modern development. Early people were assumed to have been "primitive" and so would not have possessed the technical capability for accurate surveying techniques.

Furthermore, even if the Nazca designs and lines were somehow constructed, they subsequently could only be viewed from the air. "Primitive" people were not supposed to have been capable of air travel either. Thus traditional archaeology faces a dilemma. On the one hand, the traditionalists believe that mankind has evolved up from the animal and so would have been more primitive in the past. On the other hand, evidence from the Nazca designs indicates a high technology in the past. Hence there is a dilemma.

In order to solve the Nazca dilemma, some have suggested unusual and even bizarre solutions. Erich Von Däniken, for example, proposes extraterrestrial influence.[74] In his book, *Chariots of the Gods?*, he contends

---

[74]Erich Von Däniken, *Chariots of the Gods?*, Bantam Books, Inc., New York, 1973

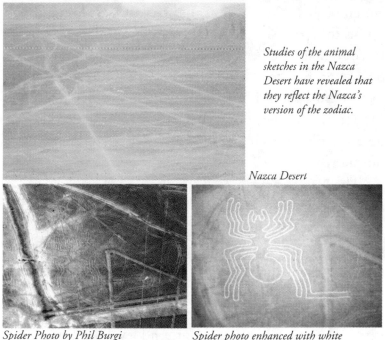

Studies of the animal sketches in the Nazca Desert have revealed that they reflect the Nazca's version of the zodiac.

Nazca Desert

Spider Photo by Phil Burgi

Spider photo enhanced with white

that the long straight lines in the Nazca desert were landing strips for space craft of aliens from space. It was a surprise to me to observe how many people actually believe that explanation.

For a number of reasons the explanation proposed by Erich Von Däniken does not make sense. Presumably the aliens would have traveled to earth by rocket ship. However, rockets take off vertically. Are we to believe that the rockets had to taxi along the ground on the "landing strips" like a propeller-driven airplane preparing to take off? Of course not.

Furthermore, there seems to be no evidence of the tremendous exhaust blast produced from a rocket. When our spacecraft rocketed to the moon, they had to land and take off again vertically from the moon. Of course, if a planet has sufficient atmosphere as does the earth, it would be possible to utilize that fact, at least for landing just as the space shuttle does. In addition many of the Nazca designs are perfectly aligned with astronomical objects. In fact, we learned from a visit to the anthropological museum in Lima that the figures in the desert were the Nazca version of the zodiac. In other words, the desert markings were used for astrological and religious purposes.

The Nazcas worshipped the sun god. They believed that when a person died, his body went back to be with the sun god. Even today the Peruvian monetary unit is the sol, or sun (coin). It is noteworthy that in order to effectively view their designs and drawings on the desert, the Nazcas would have needed to view them from above. "Kosok discovered the lines from the air and this was extremely important since at ground level the designs are nothing more than furrows, from 10 to 30 cms. deep, which run strangely across the Pampa."[75]

> Hermann Kern pointed out some years ago that it would be a good thing to write a history of 'the invisible in art.' In fact there is in various parts of the world evidence of ancient man whose common denominator was invisibility. That is to say, the magnitude of what may be created on flat land makes it impossible to be seen except from the air.[76]

The fact that the designs in the Nazca Desert can only be viewed effectively from the air should at least suggest the possibility that the constructors of the Nazca designs may have possessed the capability for

---

[75] *Las lineas Nazca*, p. 6.

[76] *Las lineas Nazca*, pp. 23-24.

flight. And yet modern secular archaeologists who believed man had evolved upward from a more primitive state were forced to deny the obvious. These modern archaeologists could not believe that people back then might have had air travel.

However, from a creationist perspective, considering man's early advanced state it might even be expected that air travel was possible back then. In fact, many years ago I even suggested that as a possibility. Archaeology had already shown us that people in early post-Flood times were technically very capable. They certainly were aware, for example, that hot air is lighter (less dense) than cold air. I speculated that the Nazcas could have constructed hot air balloons to use in viewing the designs and perhaps even as an aid in constructing the designs.

Newer research has apparently justified that speculation. By examining Nazca artifacts it has been learned that the Nazcas wove a very high quality black cloth with a very fine weave. It appears that this finely woven black cloth was used for constructing hot air balloons.[77]

> What *Kon-Tiki* uncovered about man's mastery of the sea, *Nazca* now reveals about man's conquest of the air. ...Threading through aviation's unrecorded past — and ancient legend — the adventurous team proves that men flew two thousand years ago — and they actually re-create the flying machines that ascended from Nazca's desert floor long ago. On these timeless parched plains, the project culminates in a daring and dazzling experiment that brings us face to

---

[77]Jim Woodman, *Nazca: Journey to the Sun*, New York, Pocket Books (Simon & Schuster), pp. 50-55

face with prehistoric men of stunning sophistication and intelligence![78]

When a person died, the body was placed in a basket attached to the hot air balloon. A fire was built providing hot air to cause the balloon to rise. However because the covering on the balloon was black cloth, the sun's rays striking the black cloth kept the air inside the balloon warm. In other words it was a solar-powered hot air balloon. (Even in the modern day sport of hot air ballooning, some balloons are solar powered.[79]) As the balloon and body rose up over the desert, the Nazcas claimed that the body was returning to be with the sun god. Because of the westerly-directed winds, the balloon and body were blown out over the Pacific Ocean. Then at night when the sun's rays no longer were available, the balloon crashed and the body was buried at sea.

An actual demonstration of the fact that it is possible for a hot air balloon to fly over the Nazca Desert has now been carried out. A demonstration flight was successfully made using principles and materials known to have been available to the ancient people of Nazca. Results from that demonstration led its organizer to state, "Nazca was not an ancient landing field — it was just the opposite. The lines, burn pits and 'runways' were once takeoff sites for a religion that worshipped the sun."[80]

Of course we can not return to those ancient times and actually observe what happened at Nazca. Thus we can never know for certain what occurred there. At the

---

[78]Woodman, flyleaf

[79]Woodman, p. 89.

[80]Woodman, p. 201.

very least, the modern prejudice that ancient man was "primitive" and not very capable or intelligent seems entirely wrong. In fact it may well be an example of what has been termed "temporal chauvinism."

Other artifacts suggesting that high technology existed in the past are also known. Numerous examples could be listed.

One illustration is an object cast in pure gold and found in a grave in Colombia, South America and now located in the Smithsonian Institution in Washington, D.C. It is estimated by the museum to be about 1,000 years old and is described as a "stylized insect." However gold is difficult to date closely. Nevertheless, because of its aerodynamic design, particularly the tail section with its high flanged rudder, like the tail on modern planes, the object gives the distinct impression that it is a model of an airplane. Even scientists who have closely examined the object believe that it may be an aircraft.

> Dr. Sanderson who, as a biologist, was familiar with how insects or fish *should* look, became increasingly interested in the artifact which, while certainly resembling an airplane, also included its minor attributes while *not* including those of known fish, birds or insects. For example, (on) the edges of the delta-like wings there was something clearly resembling mechanical ailerons or elevators.[81]

Of course various possible explanations other than one indicating high past technology can be and have been generated. However, when these artifacts are all

---

[81]Charles Berlitz, *Mysteries From Forgotten Worlds*, Garden City NY, Doubleday & Company, Inc., 1972, p. 30.

taken together, and associated evidences are considered, the most reasonable explanation is that these artifacts are related to past high technology.

Is evidence from the Nazca Desert and Colombia the only evidence in the Western Hemisphere of high technology in the remote past? Indeed it is not! Let us continue our investigation by examining some other ancient artifacts from South America.

This artifact is located at the Smithsonian Institution in Washington D.C. Cast in pure gold, it was found in a grave in Colombia, South America. It is estimated by the Museum to be about 1,000 years old and is described as a "stylized insect." However, because of its aerodynamic design, particularly the tail section with the elevators and high rudder, it could well represent an aircraft. (Courtesy, Dennis Swift)

CHAPTER XI

THE INCAS

Ruins from civilizations which once flourished in South America also provide us with evidence of advanced technology there in early times. In the general area of Bolivia and Peru much archaeological evidence exists relating to the Inca and even the pre-Inca civilizations. At the time of Pizarro's arrival in 1532, it has been estimated that the Inca realm extended two thousand, three hundred miles and may have had a population of from five to eight million people.

Tiahuanaco

My wife, daughter and I had the privilege of visiting some of the Inca and pre-Inca ruins. We found them to be totally fascinating. One of the ruins we visited was the ancient city of Tiahuanaco. This city was already there when the Incas came. In other words, it is pre-Inca. Invading Incas found scattered ruins whose unknown builders had long since vanished. One of the interesting features of Tiahuanaco is its location at such a high altitude —twelve thousand, five hundred feet (3,811 meters). For comparison, airplane pilots flying at that altitude for any length of time are required to wear oxygen masks. Judging from the remains, a good deal of physical effort must have been involved in constructing Tiahuanaco. The effort required seems almost impossible in view of the high altitude, and yet the city was actually built there.

The "impossible" city of Tiahuanaco in Bolivia lies at an altitude of 12,500 feet (3,810 meters). A tourist attraction at the site is the structure known as the Gateway to the Sun.

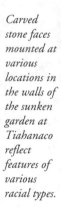

Carved stone faces mounted at various locations in the walls of the sunken garden at Tiahanaco reflect features of various racial types.

It is evident from even a cursory examination of the ruins that the builders possessed amazingly high technical skill. Large rectangular stones were not only accurately cut, but moved and placed in position with precision. Many of the larger stones had been accurately polished and were as smooth as window glass. In addition, there were no scratch marks on even the larger stones. Thus crude or "primitive" methods of moving and placing them such as dragging them, could not have been used. In fact, many of the larger stones were so smoothly polished that ones tilted to an angle of thirty or forty degrees above horizontal were used unofficially as "slides" by visiting children. They took delight in sliding down these smooth stones.

In addition to being polished to a very smooth finish, the stones at Tiahuanaco often had startlingly high quality designs carved on them. These designs were geometrically precise. I believe that even a modern jeweler could not do a better job of engraving! Even with our modern technology it would not be easy to duplicate the many accomplishments of the builders of Tiahuanaco.

One of the items tourists observe at Tiahuanaco is a large piece of rock in the shape of a doorway, known as "Gateway to the Sun." A calendar of the moon is carved on its upper surface. This and other evidence indicates that those associated with building and using Tiahuanaco were also interested in astrology just as the builders of Stonehenge and Nazca were.

There is yet a further interesting aspect of the culture belonging to those who inhabited Tiahuanaco. That aspect is learned from studying faces carved on the rocks forming part of the walls of the sunken garden located there. An examination of those faces reveals every racial type is represented.

> In a courtyard which has now been restored there is a jumble of stone heads [on the walls] which, on closer observation, appears to be made up of the most varied races, for some of the faces have narrow lips, and some swollen; some long noses, and some

hooked; some delicate ears, and some thick; some soft features, and some angular. [brackets mine][82]

(Although Erich Von Däniken's explanation or theorizing about these features may be wrong, his observations are factual.) This evidence suggests that those who inhabited Tiahuanaco either originated from a common genetic source representing all of mankind, or that they had contact and interacted with people of various racial types, or both.

I believe both possibilities above may be correct. The builders of Tiahuanaco were also descended from Noah and his sons. Even though much of the early post-Flood population was centered in and around the area of Babel, as we already mentioned earlier, people at that time were not ignorant of areas outside of Babel and the Middle East. A few may even have taken up residence in areas remote from Babel. Several lines of evidence indicate that such may indeed have been the case.[83]

Sacsahuaman

Another place of interest for us during our visit to the area was the ancient city of Sacsahuaman located near the Inca capital and present-day city of Cuzco, Peru. Stones for the edifice at Sacsahuaman were carved several miles away, hauled down and across a swamp, and then placed

---

[82]Von Däniken, p. 37.

[83]Barry Fell, *America B.C.: Ancient Settlers in the New World*, New York, Quadrangle/The New York Times Book Co., 1977;

Charles Michael Boland, *They all discovered America*, New York, Permabook, 1963;

Thomas Crawford Johnston, *Did the Phoenicians discover America?* Houston, St. Thomas Press, 1965

Sachsahuaman is located in Peru near the ancient Inca capitol city of Cuzco. Note the accuracy with which stones of widely varying sizes and shapes fit perfectly with one another. The bottom photo shows a large stone whose weight is estimated to exceed 100 tons.

in final position.[84] Many of these stones are as large, and some even larger than stones at Tiahuanaco. What im-

[84]Rene Noorbergen, *Secrets of the Lost Races: New discoveries of Advanced Technology in Ancient Civilizations*, Norcom Publishing Corp., Collegedale, TN 37315, 1977, pp. 196-197

presses an observer is the accuracy with which the stones have been carved and put into place. They are so perfectly shaped that even now after all of these intervening years, it is still not possible to insert even a strip of paper in the joints between the blocks.

Even the shapes of the stones used for constructing Sacsahuaman are fascinating. Many modern structures are monotonous and boring by comparison. To construct a wall, for example, modern builders just place one rectangular small block next to another, one after the other. However, this is not so at Sacsahuaman. These builders used their imaginations. Nearly every block was different. One person may have said, "I think this is the shape which ought to go here;" another may have said, "No, this is the shape which ought to go in this spot," and so on. Even so, with all of the variation in shapes and even after the passage of time and the probable occurrence of earthquakes, the stones are still there today fitting tightly together.

Some of the stones used in building Sacsahuaman were quite large. In the illustration, for example, my wife, daughter, and I are standing in front of a stone estimated to weigh in excess of one hundred tons. That is a large stone. However, another even larger stone is located in the area. Concerning this larger stone, one writer comments,

> What is truly impossible about the block is that it is the size of a five-story house and weighs an estimated 20,000 tons! We have no combination of machinery today that could dislodge such a weight, let alone move it any distance. The fact that the builders of Sacsahuaman could and did move this

block shows their mastery of a technology which we as yet have not attained.[85]

Moving a block weighing twenty thousand tons is indeed a significant technological achievement. Exactly how large is twenty thousand tons? The largest crane in use on earth today is capable of lifting only about three thousand tons. Yet the builders of Sacsahuaman not only could, but actually did move objects seven or eight times as large as three thousand tons. How logical is it, then, to consider those people as primitive when they could accomplish technical feats of which we moderns are not yet capable?

Evidence also indicates that the first post-Flood inhabitants in South America were technically advanced.[86] Later Inca builders utilized much of the earlier and superior technical knowledge of those that preceded them, to build their own civilization. Some of the ancients' amazing technical and engineering skills are reflected in the network of high quality canals they built. These canals were built through rugged mountain terrain to carry water for irrigation of crops.

> According to team member Charles Ortloff, a General Electric engineer, hydraulic simulations showed that the Chimu channels were completely modern in design. They relied on concepts of fluid dynamics that Western hydrologists only started to apply within the past century.[87]

---

[85]Noorbergen, p. 197

[86]Thor Heyerdahl and Arne Skjölsvold, "Archaeological Evidence of Pre-Spanish Visits to the Galapagos Islands," *Mem. No. 12, Society for American Archaeology* 1956

[87]Peter Gwynne, "Earth's seismicity destroyed Chimu irrigation system" *Industrial Research & Development*, September 1982, p. 59.

As a matter of fact, modern day scientists study these canals to learn how to successfully build modern canals in the same area. Some of the ancient Inca-built canals have even been cleaned up and are in use again now.[88]

An interesting example of the fact that much advanced technology from the past has been lost is the result of the reintroduction of ancient farming methods near Tiahuanaco.

> In a remarkable example of 'experimental archaeology,' Alan Kolata and his colleagues at the University of Chicago reproduced the irrigation technology practiced 1,500 years ago by the Tiahuanaco people in test plots near modern-day Bolivia's Lake Titicaca. The resulting bumper crops — in some cases seven times the average yield of land farmed using modern techniques — suggest that this long-lost method of constructing raised fields among irrigation channels could have allowed more than 100,000 people to thrive more than a millennium ago in a region that now supports approximately 7,000.[89]

This example is not unique.

In view of evidence that past civilizations were not necessarily "primitive," perhaps we moderns would do well to be a bit more humble in asserting that the ancients could not have been as smart or advanced as we imagine ourselves to be. Is evidence of high technical capability limited only to South America? What is observed as we move further north?

[88]William F. Allman with Joannie M. Schrof, "Lost Empires of the Americas" *U.S. News & World Report*, April 2, 1990, p. 47.

[89]Allman and Schrof, "Lost Empires of the Americas" *U.S. News & World Report*, April 2, 1990, p. 53.

CHAPTER XII

THE MAYA

M oving further northward into Central America, we encounter the land of the Maya on the Yucatan Peninsula. The cities of the ancient Maya lie in ruins and are now covered by jungle growth. Much exploration of these ruins has been carried out in the last several decades. New explorations as well as information already available from past studies have revealed that the Maya culture possessed not only a high level of technical sophistication, but also had a preoccupation with astronomical measurements.

For example, at Chichen Itza, a place frequented by tourists, remains of an observatory are found. In overall appearance, the observatory at Chichen Itza is reminiscent of a modern astronomical observatory. From this observatory the Mayans made amazingly accurate astronomical measurements rivaling our best modern values. It is assumed by those who view man as more primitive in the past that the Mayans' accurate astronomical measurements were made using only the primitive method of peering through cracks in the observatory, but this assumption conflicts with remaining records which reveal surprisingly great accuracy to the Mayan measurements. Not only were the vernal and autumnal equinoxes recorded accurately, but the length of the solar day was measured to an accuracy of seven significant figures.[90] It

---

[90]Graham Hancock, p. 159

is difficult to imagine how the crude method of peering through cracks could result in such accuracy. Perhaps the Mayans may have possessed technology for making accurate measuring instruments and we have not yet discovered them or the instruments were not preserved. Another possibility is that the instruments were actually discovered but were not recognized as such. They may then have been destroyed or even melted down by Spanish conquistadors or others for their precious metal content.

Using their accurate solar measurements, the Mayans constructed a very accurate calendar.[91] Examples of those stone calendars still exist. Although these calendars utilize the base twenty number system instead of the base ten number system we use, and although the calendars were written using a script similar to hieroglyphics, these calendars still function accurately right up to the present. In fact the Mayan calendar is more accurate than the one we currently use. Concerning the number of days in a year,

> In modern Western society we still make use of a solar calendar which was introduced in Europe in 1582 and is based on the best scientific knowledge then available: the famous Gregorian calendar. ... Pope Gregory XIII's reform substituted a finer and more accurate calculation: 365.2425 days. Thanks to scientific advances since 1582 we now know that the *exact* length of the solar year is 365.2422 days. ... Strangely enough, though its origins are wrapped in the mists of antiquity far deeper than the sixteenth century, the

---

[91]Silvanus Morley, *The Ancient Maya*, Stanford University Press, 1956, pp. 256-257

Mayan calendar achieved even greater accuracy. It calculated the solar year at 365.2420 days, a minus error of only 0.0002 of a day.[92]

It comes as a surprise to modern people to learn that the Mayan Calendar is more accurate than the one we use, the Gregorian calendar. It was more accurate by a factor of about ten. For example, when someone is asked the number of days in a year on our "modern" calendar, the answer is usually 365. But of course this is not completely correct because the actual value is closer to $365\frac{1}{4}$. Thus in order to prevent our calendar from becoming out of synchronization with actual astronomical values, it is necessary every four years for us to add an extra day during the month of February. The year in which this is done is known as a leap year. However, even this does not correct our calendar exactly, and each century year it is necessary to add the extra day only if the year is divisible by 400. In other words, our modern calendar is in continual need of correction to keep it synchronized with astronomical reality.

Although the Mayans eventually came to believe that time was cyclical, they nevertheless calibrated their calendar with creation. The year zero on the Mayan calendar was the creation of the world.[93] This fact has resulted in a puzzle for those who hold that man ascended up from the animal over millions of years of time. It is now recognized that the Mayans apparently kept the most accurate time the world has ever known.[94]

---

[92]Graham Hancock, p. 159

[93]Morley, *The Ancient Maya*, Stanford University Press, 1956, p. 242

[94]Morley, *The Ancient Maya*, Stanford University Press, 1956, p. 234-237

In overall appearance the Mayan Observatory at Chichen Itza is reminiscent of a modern observatory. Using astronomical measurements, the Mayans constructed a calendar which was more accurate than our own.

Photo by Steven and Carla Allemann

Yet the year zero on the Mayan calendar, the creation of the world, agrees with the Biblical time scale. It agrees, in fact, to within about fifty-six years of Ussher's famous chronology. It was 56 years shorter than the 4004 B.C. of Ussher. Reliable historical records from other cultures, although pagan and supposedly having no knowledge of Genesis also concur with the Genesis date of creation of about 4000 B.C.[95] For modern secular archaeologists such a recent date for the origin of the world is totally unacceptable, so they invent other "more reasonable" possible explanations. However in rejecting such data, they are then faced with a gigantic puzzle: how could the Mayans, who kept the most accurate time the world has ever known, have been so very wrong concerning the age

---

[95]Bill Cooper, *After the Flood: The Early post-Flood History of Europe*, New Wine Press, West Sussex, pp. 127-128

of the earth? Maybe the Mayans were not so wrong after all! Could it be that the assumption of man ascending up from animals over millions of years is wrong instead?

Also, as is well known, the Mayans built pyramids and associated them with astronomical objects. For example, the chief temple at Chichen Itza has 365 steps leading to its top. Why are there 365 steps? The obvious answer is that there is one step for each whole day of the year.[96]

In spite of their brilliance, the Mayans rejected the worship of the One True God. Their preoccupation with stars led them into pantheistic astrology and degenerate forms of worship. As part of their religious ceremonies, the Mayans also carried out human sacrifices at the temple entrance. [97] Priests tore out the hearts of human beings placed on the altar. The goal was to cut the heart out so quickly that it would still be beating as the priests held it up for eagles to carry off and eat. Their religious practices were cruel, vicious and degrading.

Traditional archaeologists have assumed that only a "primitive" technology was possessed by the Mayans. It has been assumed, for example, that Maya culture did not know of the important invention of the wheel so necessary for the development of higher technology. Yet the curious fact remains that the Mayans used wheels on what appear to be toys. Hancock comments on this fact.

> Soon afterwards the American archaeologist made a second unsettling discovery at Tres Zapotes: children's toys in the form of little wheeled dogs. These cute artefacts conflicted head-on with prevailing archaeo-

[96]*Chichen Itza*, Ediciones Alducin, Mexico, 1984, pp. 45-46
[97]Morley, *The Ancient Maya*, Stanford University Press, 1956, pp. 184-187

Wheeled dog toy found in Mexico

Photo by Helen Culp

logical opinion, which held that the wheel had remained undiscovered in Central America until the time of the conquest. The 'dogmobiles' proved, at the very least, that the *principle* of the wheel had been known to the Olmecs, Central America's earliest civilization. And if a people as resourceful as the Olmecs had worked out the principle of the wheel, it seemed highly unlikely that they would have used it just for children's toys.[98]

The pieces of the puzzle when assembled show a unified picture. Let us draw back as it were and view the whole picture. What will the picture show as we summarize the details we have been discussing?

[98]Hancock, p. 122

A RECURRING THEME

As evidence relating to ancient man, for example, OOPArts and other artifacts, is examined, a recurring pattern emerges. The pattern indicates that these artifacts originated in an early civilization. They were man-made and not the product of aliens from space. However, the history of the discoveries and technological developments leading up to the production of sophisticated items known as OOPArts has been largely lost. Perhaps a sudden catastrophe caused the loss. One writer makes the following observation. "The unprecedented explosion of knowledge 5,000 years ago, they [historians] believe, may have been foreshadowed by an earlier society whose cultural remnants have long since vanished."[99] It is interesting to note the figure "5,000 years ago." That is 3,000 B.C. and is about the time of the tower of Babel.

Another author who summarizes much information from a study of OOPArts also indicates that they were in fact man-made.

> Today's bookstores are plentifully stocked with books written by persons trying to connect the ooparts with visits of beings from other galaxies who supposedly toured this planet more than 10,000 years ago, leaving behind proof of their transgalactic visitation. The major difficulty in accepting this theory is that none

---

[99]Robert Patton, "OOPArts," *Omni*, September 1982, p. 54.

of the ooparts is composed of material unknown on earth, and their technological make-up conforms with the development of our own modern civilization. A closer look at the strange artifacts now suggests that the ooparts originated in a man-made civilization - one that antedated known history - one that attained an elevated degree of development, but was destroyed to such an extent by a devastating catastrophe in the distant past that only a few remnants of its science and technology survived among the inferior cultures that succeeded it in history.[100]

Survivors of the great catastrophe in the past reappeared in the Middle East area around the eastern end of the Mediterranean Sea. Then a subsequent sudden scattering of people out from that area occurred. How may all these pieces of the puzzle of ancient man be explained? The Bible provides a basis for an answer.

According to Scripture, man was created in a state of perfection, but fell from that state by rebelling against the Creator. In spite of undergoing a continuing process of spiritual, moral, physical and mental degeneration as a consequence of the Fall, early man was highly capable. He was not "primitive" in any sense. On the contrary, early man began to rapidly develop a high civilization. Scripture (Genesis, chapter four) informs us that by only the seventh generation from Adam, they had developed organized agriculture, metallurgy, musical instruments, government structure, and arts.

Although that pre-Flood civilization developed to an advanced degree technologically, it was spiritually and

---

[100]Rene Noorbergen, *Secrets of the Lost Races: New Discoveries of Advanced Technology in Ancient Civilizations*, Collegedale TN, Norcom Publishing Corp., 1992, p. 3.

morally degenerate. The Creator eventually sent a Flood which destroyed it all. All of that pre-Flood civilization and its technology was destroyed, but not the memory that it could be done. Some of the pre-Flood technology may even have been taken on board the Ark. Certainly Noah and his family knew of the antediluvian technology and remembered it. They may even have made written records of much of it. After the Flood it was necessary for the post-diluvians to rebuild, but they did not have to rediscover or reinvent the pre-Flood technology.

Thus during the post-Flood rapid population increase, there was again the emergence of a technically advanced civilization under the leadership of Nimrod and located in the area of Mesopotamia in the region of the globe where the Ark landed. It is known to us as the ancient Sumerian civilization. However, because of rebellion against the Creator's post-Flood command to disperse out over the earth, language was confounded into many separate ones from the one original common language which everyone spoke.

The list of various tribes and nations which developed after the Flood and the account of the origin of various languages is recorded in Genesis chapter ten up through chapter eleven, verse nine. Thus the Bible provides an outline of history and a basis for assembling the puzzle pieces.

Upon dispersing from the Babel area, each language group sought to establish its own culture. However, the pagan religious system associated with astrology, along with many other ideas inherited from Babel, were carried along and in various ways incorporated into the developing culture of each dispersed group. Thus the use of astrological symbols, the construction of large edifices such as henges, pyramids, and observatories were associated with the new cultural centers being established at various locations around the globe. Research has established that these widely separated cultural center locations all appear to have begun at roughly the same time.

There is also the common observation of the sudden appearance of highly developed technology with no experimentation, learning, and development period. The reason for this sudden appearance of highly developed culture at various geographic locations is that the technical base utilized by these cultures was in fact developed at Babel before the dispersion. As each new culture became seeded in its own area, it had the potential to utilize and built upon a technological base it brought with it from Babel. In more recent times, a similar sequence of events occurred when settlers from Europe colonized North America. The settlers brought with them technologies from their homeland and then built upon that base in the New World.

The Scriptures thus provide an accurate account of early post-Flood history and an explanation of many archaeological puzzles relating to world-wide patterns of ancient high technology.

Message to Moderns

Not only does Scripture provide archaeological answers, but it also predicts future developments. In this connection, there is an important message to our own modern day to be learned from the puzzle of ancient man. Jesus told His disciples that even though He was going to leave them and return to the Father, one future day He would return. The disciples were curious to know what indications or signs there would be to indicate the time of Jesus' return. They asked, "What shall be the sign of thy coming, and of the end of the world?" (Matt. 24:3). His answer was,

> But of that day and hour knoweth no man, no, not the angels of heaven, but my Father only. But as the days of Noe (Noah) were, so shall also the coming of the Son of man be. For as in the days that were before the flood they were eating and drinking, marrying and giving in marriage, until the day that Noe entered into the ark, And knew not until the flood came, and took them all away; so shall also the coming of the Son of man be. (Matt. 24:36-39)

There is much more involved in this answer from Jesus than we will take time to comment on here. However, several points are especially worth noting in light of our present study. First, the exact day or time of Christ's return will not be known. Nevertheless there will be some indications. "But as the days of Noe were, so shall also the coming of the Son of man be." Then after stating this, Jesus reviews and provides a summary of conditions prevailing during Noah's time specifically mentioning several points.

A few additional details are provided in the parallel passage from Luke's gospel.

> Likewise also as it was in the days of Lot; they did eat, they drank, they bought, they sold, they planted, they builded; But the same day that Lot went out of Sodom it rained fire and brimstone from heaven, and destroyed them all. Even thus shall it be in the day when the Son of man is revealed. (Luke 17:28-30)

Let us briefly review conditions in that time of Noah to which Jesus refers. Because of prolonged child-bearing years and long lifetimes, world population had grown to be quite large. There was a rapid rise in population. A high level of science and technology had been developed. Mankind, however, was in rebellion against the Creator and was using his technology to "fill the world with violence." Even though they had knowledge of the one true Creator God, they ignored Him and His precepts. Their thoughts and concerns were "only evil continually" (Genesis 6:5). Day-to-day concerns of business and pleasure totally occupied their minds. They ate, they drank, they married, they bought and they sold. There was no time or room for God in their thoughts.

The epistle of Jude summarizes spiritual and moral conditions before the Flood: "And Enoch also, the seventh from Adam, prophesied of these, saying, Behold, the Lord cometh with ten thousands of his saints, To execute judgment upon all, and to convince all that are ungodly among them of all their ungodly deeds which they have ungodly committed, and of all their hard speeches which ungodly sinners have spoken against him. These are murmurers, complainers, walking after their own lusts; and their mouth speaketh great swelling words, having men's persons in admiration because of advantage." (Jude 14-16) In addition to being totally preoccupied with temporal things, the pre-Flood populace was adequately warned through the preaching of Noah of a coming judgment. (II Peter 2:5) Yet they ignored the warning and continued in their ungodly lifestyles.

It is apparent that there are many similarities between the days of Noah and current culture worldwide. The twentieth century has been the most violent in recorded history. Not only have there been wars with unprecedented violence, but violence and terrorism seem to be rapidly increasing worldwide. Crime and personal violence also seem to be at an all-time high.

In addition, the rapid rise in technology during the twentieth century is no less than astounding. Also there has been a rapid rise in world population. But at the same time, modern communication technology has allowed the Gospel of the Lord Jesus Christ and Biblical knowledge to be broadly disseminated through these technological means and through preaching. The world has been warned of coming judgment, but the warning largely goes unheeded and is ignored. Scriptural principles for living are disdained by most of the world's leaders. With the many similarities between our own time and the days of Noah, could not the return of Christ also be close at hand? It would appear so. Even so, come, Lord Jesus! Amen.

PART TWO

CHAPTER XIV

BIAS, SCIENCE, AND RELIGION

Any discussion of the origin and history of man involves weighty religious, philosophical, and scientific issues and can elicit strong emotions. In fact it has been my observation that such a discussion can easily degenerate into one generating more heat than light. The reason for this is that people often enter the discussion while holding completely different and conflicting world views. However, a much more calm and rational discussion is possible when the participants are able to recognize and appreciate the influence of a worldview.

It is my hope that the following discussion relating to worldviews and associated items will aid the reader not only in better understanding his own position, but also in any discussion of it with others. It should aid in answering questions such as, "Is the Bible against science?" "Can an explanation using information from the Bible be scientific?"

Bias in science

In the introduction I stated that there are two possible approaches for explaining the origin of man, supernatural and natural. One or the other of these two beginning points is used in any explanation for human origins.

The beginning point for thinking about origins constitutes a bias. Scientists are biased. Everyone is! Anyone who thinks logically is biased. In fact, it is not possible even to think without being biased. We will now show how the two views about how man originated, creation or evolution, result from two different biases.

Because I personally believe in creation, when I lecture on the topic of origins some in my audience accuse me of being biased. They are absolutely correct. The issue is not whether a scientist (or anyone) is biased, but which bias or faith best conforms to reality.

The reason for the necessity of bias is that sound thinking involves logic, and therefore bias. This concept can best be grasped with the aid of a diagram, as illustrated in Figure 1.

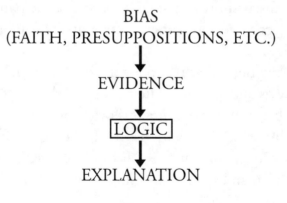

Figure 1

Logic, we remember, is the set of rules for correct thinking. For example, one of the very foundational rules in logic is the law of non-contradiction. This law states that it is not possible for two opposite or contradictory statements to both be true at the same time. To illustrate, suppose someone states, "There is a sailboat on this lake," but someone else at the same time states, "There are <u>no</u> sailboats on this lake." These are contradictory statements. The law of non-contradiction tells us that these statements cannot both be true at the same time. When the law of non-contradiction is violated, then the correctness of a logical conclusion or explanation is immediately brought into question.

To provide an analogy, correct thinking using the rules of logic can be compared to the way a computer processes information. A computer has been designed so as to rigorously follow the rules of logic and these rules are absolute. An electronic switch, for example, is either on or off. The switch follows the law of non-contradiction. It cannot be both on and off at the same time.

Even though a computer rigidly and mechanically follows the rules of logic, it still may not yield a correct result. It might function entirely correctly using all of the rules of logic and still not yield a correct result. How can this be? The reason is that logic alone is not sufficient. There must also be input to the computer. It needs a starting point. If poor or defective information is fed into a computer, output from the computer will also be poor. It must have the correct starting point (bias) for its "thinking." As is well known in computer circles, the starting point or input for a computer affects its output. It is the basis for the often-repeated phrase, "Garbage in, garbage out." A computer's output will be no more correct than its input even though it rigorously follows the rules of logic. The human mind behaves similarly.

Thus, in order to arrive at a correct explanation involving some particular data or evidence, it is necessary not only to follow the rules of logic, but also to have a correct <u>starting</u> point or bias for thinking. As already stated, a person's starting point for thinking is known as his *bias* and it is not possible even to think about something without having a bias. Note that other terms are frequently used to describe bias, the starting point for thinking. Sometimes the starting point is called faith or presuppositions or axioms or postulates or assumptions. In our discussion, we will use the term *bias*.

Why is it necessary to have a bias? The diagram in Figure 2 will aid in answering this question. The circle represents all available knowledge. Everything which can be known is inside the circle. Let the smaller circle inside the larger circle represent the fraction of total available knowledge which I (for example) know. In reality, I know only a tiny fraction of total knowledge. In fact, compared to what there is to know, I know such a tiny fraction that it was necessary to exaggerate the size of the small circle representing what I know. If the circle size were in correct proportion, it would be so small as to be almost invisible. Thus it was necessary to exaggerate its size so as to be easily seen. I am not unique. The same limitations apply to every other human being as well.

Even the smartest and most educated individuals know only a tiny fraction of total knowledge. Therefore because we as individuals each know only a tiny fraction of what there is to know, we must have a starting point for thinking. We must have <u>faith</u> in the correctness of our starting point. That is our bias. Only an infinite Mind could legitimately claim to know all knowledge. Only the Creator has all knowledge. Only the Creator could know that a certain starting point was absolutely correct with no uncertainty or element of faith necessary. For finite humans with limited knowledge, faith or bias is therefore necessary.

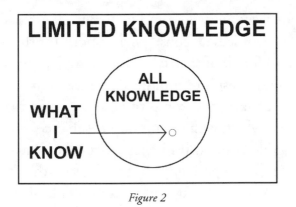

Figure 2

Thinking and logic

Thinking involves more than rules and a starting point. These are not enough. We always think <u>about something</u> (facts, data, etc.). In other words, in addition to the rules of logic and a starting point, thinking also has content and an end point or conclusion. The content is the subject matter under discussion, as for example, ancient man, our subject here. Remember, the starting point for logic often goes by different terms such as assumptions, axioms, postulates, or presuppositions. Correct thinking must: follow the rules of logic, include a starting point (or bias), be based on true information, and reach a conclusion. This whole package is often referred to as a paradigm.

At this point, some may wonder whether or not one <u>must</u> draw a conclusion. The answer in the case for the origin of man is that it is not possible to avoid drawing a conclusion. Even deciding not to "decide" constitutes a decision.

Who is Man?

One's views on where and how man originated have direct and immediate consequences both for the individual and for all of society. If, for example, human beings are the result of mindless processes of chance and time, then another person is of no more value than any other item which is the result of pure chance, for example, a pile of junk. If I believe that others have little value, then I will probably treat them accordingly. I will be part of what I like to refer to as the "cult of rudeness" in modern culture.

On the other hand, if we believe that we were specially created in the image of the Creator and are therefore morally responsible to Him, we will approach life and others from that perspective. Thus we cannot "decide" to "not decide" because in reality we carry out our daily lives based on one conclusion or the other.

The paradigm

Individual scientific facts or data are like pieces of a jigsaw puzzle. The goal is to assemble the pieces so as to obtain a complete picture. Of course when assembling an actual jigsaw puzzle, one uses logic to decide whether to pick up a particular piece and experiment with it to find out if it fits into the puzzle at a certain spot. Similarly, scientists use logic to attempt to fit scientific observations into an overall picture or paradigm.

Nicholas Wade, in reviewing *The Structure of Scien-*

tific Revolutions by Thomas Kuhn, says: "...scientists are guided by a set of theories, standards, and methods which Kuhn refers to as a 'paradigm.'"[101] (Thomas Kuhn is a well-known theorist and historian of science and has clearly and carefully pointed out the function of a paradigm.) Continuing, the reviewer then states,

> Logic and experiment, says Kuhn, are not sufficient: 'The competition between paradigms is not the sort of battle that can be resolved by proofs.' In fact the transfer of allegiance from one paradigm to another 'is a conversion experience that cannot be forced.' The grounds for conversion may include arguments that 'appeal to the individual's sense of the appropriate or the aesthetic,' and faith that the new paradigm will be better able to resolve the anomalies that precipitated the crisis. ... the emphasis of Kuhn's thesis is that logic alone cannot be decisive in a choice between theories.[102]

The reviewer readily identified a key point: logic alone is not enough. Logic is only one component of a paradigm.

Is logic absolute?

Logic, as already discussed, is the set of rules for correct thinking. These rules are absolute. Man did not invent them, but only discovered them. I believe these rules were given to us by the Creator and are therefore absolute and not a matter of one's opinion. Some would even attempt to deny that the rules of logic are absolute.

---

[101]Nicholas Wade, "Thomas S. Kuhn: Revolutionary Theorist of Science," *Science*, 8 July 1977, p. 144.

[102]Wade, pp. 144-145.

They would for example attempt to deny the law of non-contradiction. As previously mentioned, this law states that it is not possible for both a statement and its opposite to be true at the same time. However, this law of logic is undeniable. It cannot even be denied, for in order to deny it one must use the rules of logic and the law of non-contradiction itself to deny the law of non-contradiction. Thus the law of non-contradiction is undeniable. The rules of logic are absolute.

A further illustration is the case of those who insist that absolute truth does not exist. Note their problem. They want us to accept as absolutely true that no absolute truth exists! They have used a statement which they want us to believe is absolutely true to deny any statement can be absolutely true. Thus they have violated the law of non-contradiction. As can be seen just from this example, this basic law of logic is absolute and undeniable. One must use logic even to deny logic.

The Place of Evidence

For the origin of man, the view that man was directly created and the view that he was not directly created cannot both be true at the same time. If one is true, the other must be false. If such is the case, then could not the issue be resolved by appealing to the available scientific evidence? Although that suggestion is often made, the answer is clearly, "No! Appealing to scientific evidence will not resolve the issue." Let us examine why.

Actual observational data of science are not the problem. It is important to emphasize that point. Potentially at least, all scientists have the same data available to them. The problem is <u>not</u> with the data. Instead, the problem is with how the data are <u>interpreted</u>. What do the actual facts (observed data) mean? How should we view them? How are they to be explained?

Figure 3 illustrates in diagram form the reason evidence or data or facts alone are not sufficient to resolve the issue.

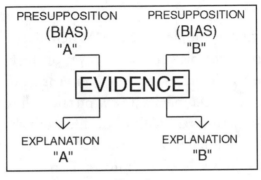

Figure 3

If we start with assumptions or presuppositions (bias) labeled "A" and we look at the data (evidence), then using logic we will come up with a corresponding set of conclusions which we label "A." On the other hand, someone else using a different set of assumptions or presuppositions, labeled "B" looking at the same data or evidence and using equally valid logic will come up with a different set of conclusions, labeled "B."

For any evidence it is always possible to invent an explanation different from the explanation under discussion. All that is necessary to do that is to <u>begin</u> thinking using a different bias. The question is not whether another explanation for any given evidence is possible, because it is possible. As Phillip Johnson, a specialist on logic, has accurately pointed out, "the conflict (evolutionism / creationism) is not over 'facts' but over ways of thinking."[103] That is the reason an issue cannot simply be resolved by an appeal to the evidence. Instead, the question is whether the new explanation is true, whether it agrees with reality.

Returning to our puzzle analogy, each scientific fact (observational data) is like one piece of the puzzle. Let us picture mentally the pieces of a puzzle as all spread out on a table. Our goal will be to assemble them into a whole, giving a complete picture. When assembling a jigsaw puzzle, the picture on the cover of the box from which the puzzle pieces came can serve as a guide. Those who have ever assembled a jigsaw puzzle will remember that it is sometimes difficult to decide from shape alone where an individual puzzle piece will fit. Additional information is needed. This information can be supplied from the colors and markings on the puzzle piece which can be matched with the picture on the box to give the additional information about where the puzzle piece might fit. The box cover picture (reality) also gives assurance that the puzzle pieces will all fit together so as to form a complete picture. Similarly we wish to fit available scientific facts together into a whole picture, especially those relating to man's origin. In accomplishing this task a guide is needed to serve the same purpose as does a picture on a puzzle box.

Is naturalism true?

In the case of man's origin, two pictures, as it were, are being suggested as correct. One picture is by God the Designer and Creator and the other is naturalism, usually

---

[103]Phillip E. Johnson, "Shouting 'Heresy' in the Temple of Darwin" *Christianity Today* October 24, 1994, p. 26.

in the form of Darwinism or one of the updated versions of it.

By way of review, a clear definition of the term *naturalism* may aid our ensuing discussion. A dictionary definition is "in *philosophy*, the belief that the natural world is the whole of reality and that there is no supernatural or spiritual creation, value, control, or significance: it holds that scientific laws can explain all phenomena. ... in *religion*, the doctrine that religion does not depend on supernatural experience, divine revelation, etc., and that all religious truth may be derived from the natural world."[104]

Within the religious community there is also suggested a picture made by mixing pictures from two different box covers, as it were. One picture is from theism and the other is from naturalism. However, there are two serious problems with this approach. One is its conflict with reality, and the second is its violation of the laws of logic. "Theistic naturalism," as the attempted compromise has been called,[105] will be discussed in further detail in the next chapter. It will be shown there why this approach cannot work.

For the most part, current culture either ignores altogether the Biblical picture, or else refuses to consider its explanation for man's origin on the grounds that it is "religious" and therefore not a true account of history. The "religious" explanation is viewed as mythical and unreal. Only some evolutionary (naturalistic) account for

---

[104]Joseph H. Friend and David B. Guralnik, Ed., *Webster's New World Dictionary of the American Language*, College Edition, The World Publishing Company, Cleveland and New York, 1955, p. 978

[105]Phillip E. Johnson, *Reason in the Balance*, Downers Grove IL, InterVarsity Press, 1995, p. 97.

man's origin is allowed because it is supposedly "scientific" and therefore true. Because this prejudice and this fallacy are so commonly encountered, it is well for us to examine this point in a bit more detail now.

Phillip E. Johnson, professor of law at the University of California at Berkeley and a specialist in logic has thoroughly analyzed contemporary naturalism and its claims.[106] During an interview about his work, Dr. Johnson stated, "I insisted upon asking whether naturalism is true, even though the immediate response from critics was that to ask such a question showed I did not 'understand how science works.'"[107]

Again during an interview about his book *Reason in the Balance: The Case Against Naturalism in Science, Law, and Education*, Phillip Johnson stated concerning naturalists,

> They think they don't have a philosophy. They just peer directly into reality. This is, of course, the great mistake of which they've got to be disabused. ... Look, rather, at those presuppositions which everyone takes for grated, and which therefore are never mentioned. Those unspoken things will be much more important. In our current scientific culture, and really in the university culture outside the sciences, too, the unspoken presupposition is naturalism. Naturalism is the way to understand reality. But once that's seen as a philosophy, and asked to justify itself, naturalists are absolutely baffled. To the metaphysical naturalist, to

---

[106]Phillip E. Johnson, *Darwin On Trial*, Downers Grove IL, InterVarsity Press, 1993, and *Reason in the Balance*, 1995

[107]Phillip E. Johnson, "Shouting 'Heresy' in the Temple of Darwin" *Christianity Today*, October 24, 1994, p. 25.

ask, 'Is naturalism true?' is like asking, 'Is truth true?'[108]

Continuing with the interview, Dr. Johnson provides a summary and also outlines a distressing possibility.

> Now, with respect to an issue like creationism, the typical fair-minded liberal rationalist will say, 'We have nothing against creationism, but it should stay in the churches. It doesn't belong in science classrooms — because science classrooms are where we indoctrinate the children of the creationists so we won't have this problem to deal with in the next generation.' They don't realize that they're saying one position is true and rational, and the other, false and irrational — and that the false and irrational one should be eliminated. Peacefully, gently, gradually eliminated, if possible, not by firing squads and concentration camps. Although, if the level of frustration rises, one never knows what measures might be needed.[109]

Those last comments are sobering thoughts indeed!

The issue of man's origin finally boils down to what shall be used as a standard for measuring ultimate truth. Those committed to naturalism use the filter of naturalism to test all ideas for truth content. Any idea or paradigm which does not agree with the tenets of naturalism is judged as untrue, or else is explained away using naturalistic terms.

Those who hold to the naturalistic view of origins (evolutionism, man up from an animal) insist that only

---

[108] "Putting Reason in the Balance: An Interview with Phillip E. Johnson" *Bible-Science News*, September 1995, p. 2.

[109] "Putting Reason in the Balance: An Interview with Phillip E. Johnson" *Bible-Science News*, September 1995, p. 4

their view is scientific, and the alternate view, supernatural creation, is only religion and therefore untrue.

> For those who have chosen to devote their lives to exploring exactly how humans evolved from apes, persons who doubt the basic premise are by definition creationists, and hence not to be taken seriously. That there might be no reliable fossil evidence of human evolution is out of the question.[110]

This prejudiced view has been exposed by numerous creation/evolution discussions and debates. As an example, the well-credentialed university professor, Dr. Niall Shanks made such a prejudiced claim during a public debate with Dr. Duane Gish of the Institute for Creation Research.

> He began by asserting that evolution is the only acceptable scientific theory of origins since, he claimed, creation is nothing more than religion. This is the theme incessantly promoted by the N.C.S.E. and evolutionists in general.[111]

(N.C.S.E. is National Center for Science Education, headed by Dr. Eugenie Scott.)

Intellectual bullying

Such claims by those who hold to naturalism not only are a self-serving logical fallacy, but amount to intellectual bullying toward those who would hold or consider holding contrary views. Those who hold to

---

[110]Johnson, Darwin On Trial, p. 81.

[111] "Debate at East Tennessee State University" *Acts & Facts*, July 1996, p. 2

naturalistic philosophy <u>define</u> a scientific explanation as a naturalistic explanation. By their definition then, the creation explanation is not scientific. Creation is termed a "religious" explanation and is therefore considered as untrue. The logical fallacy of this claim by those who are committed to naturalism is evident when one takes a moment to consider the naturalists' methodology. The same methodology could be used against naturalism. A creationist could define a scientific explanation for origins as creation. By definition then, a naturalistic explanation would be unscientific and therefore considered as untrue.

The origin of the universe and man has not been scientifically observed. Naturalism is only a <u>belief</u> about the origin of all things. In effect it is a religious statement. From a purely logical viewpoint, man was either supernaturally created or he was not. Obviously then one possibility is that man originated by supernatural creation. Any search for truth carried out in an objective manner must consider both available options. If creation is what actually happened, then as a result it is the true explanation. In this case the claim of naturalism that creation is unscientific turns out to be the same as admitting that naturalism is not seeking truth, but only avoiding creation. Objectivity has been rejected. Whatever label is placed on creationism, "scientific" or "religious" is irrelevant. The meaning of these terms depends on how they are defined. The real point is whether creation or naturalism is the true explanation. If creation is the true explanation for man's origin, (and naturalism cannot prove that it is not) then it may properly be termed scientific. Even if creation is possibly true, it may properly be termed scientific.

The Bible vs. Naturalism

As mentioned earlier, two pictures or possibilities are being suggested for the origin of man. One is the Bible and the other is naturalism. Why do we list only these two possibilities? The reason is that a careful study and thorough analysis has shown that this is the case. One individual, among others, who has carried out such a thorough study is David Noebel.

David Noebel has worked in Summit Ministries for over thirty years. At Summit Ministries, teenagers receive in-depth training on the topic of Christianity versus competing world views. Noebel refers to the battle between Christianity and opposing world views as the "Second Great Civil War." He states,

> To be more precise, it is a battle between worldviews. On one side is the Christian worldview. On the other is the Humanist worldview divided into three easily definable branches: Secular Humanism, Marxism/ Leninism, and Cosmic Humanism or the New Age movement. While the latter three don't agree in every detail, there is one point on which they unanimously concur—their opposition to Biblical Christianity.[112]

Naturalism, or as Noebel refers to it, Humanism, is diametrically opposed to Biblical Christianity including the Scriptural account of man's origin. However for those committed to Biblical Christianity, the Holy Scripture is the ultimate test of truth. All ideas are compared to Scripture, and whatever does not agree is wrong and

---

[112]David A. Noebel, *Understanding the Times*, Summit Press, Manitou Springs, CO, 1991, p. 7

untrue because the Creator would not lie to us. Again Noebel observes,

> Christianity...is the only worldview that provides a consistent explanation of all the facts of reality with regard to theology, philosophy, ethics, economics, or anything else. As Carl Henry says, 'The Christian belief system, which the Christian knows to be grounded in divine revelation, is relevant to all of life.' This relevance results from the fact that Christianity is, we believe, the one worldview based on truth. 'Christianity is true,' says George F. Gilder, author of *Wealth and Poverty*, 'and its truth will be discovered anywhere you look very far.'[113]

Again commenting on using the Scripture as standard for truth, Noebel states,

> When presenting the Christian worldview, then, we take the Bible at face value. Call it 'literal' interpretation if you wish, but it is difficult to see how else the writers of the Old and New Testaments meant [themselves] to be taken. Figures of speech, yes; typologies, yes; analogies, yes; but overall they wrote in simple, straightforward terms. When a writer says, 'In the beginning God created the heavens and the earth,' we understand him to say that there is a God, there was a beginning to creation, that heaven and earth exist, and that God made them. When a writer says, 'God so loved the world that he gave his only begotten Son that whosoever believeth on him shall not perish but have everlasting life,' we understand him to say that there is a God, that God loves, that God sent His Son, and that those who believe Him shall not perish but

---

have everlasting life. It does not take a Ph.D. or a high IQ to comprehend the basic message of the Bible. God's special revelation is open to everyone.[114]

Either one uses the Scriptures as the absolute standard of all truth, or he uses some other presuppositional system generated by man's mind as the absolute standard.

Thus we are faced with two pictures on the box, as it were, for putting the puzzle pieces together. One comes from Scripture given to us as absolute truth by the Creator. The second presupposes that Scripture is not the source of absolute truth, but that man must decide for himself what is true. As Noebel has emphasized, one or the other of these two views is held by people in today's world.[115]

Concerning the topic of origins, one may often discern whether Scripture, or the opinion of men, is being used as the ultimate standard for truth. The remark, "Science says" is a tip-off that man's opinion is the test of truth rather than Scripture. When the term "science says" is used, it is almost a certainty that "science" is being equated with naturalism. On the other hand when someone says, "Scripture says" it is probable that person is using the Creator's word as standard for truth.

In Chapter 15, actual evidence is examined to see how it matches with the two pictures — theism and naturalism.

[114]Noebel, p. 40

[115]Noebel, *Understanding the Times*

CHAPTER XV

NATURALISM'S PICTURE

Chapter 14 laid a foundation for discussing the place of evidence, logic, and bias in any discussion of ancient man. We noted that in current culture, two competing pictures, Creationism and Naturalism, are being presented for explaining man's origin. By the rules of logic, specifically the law of non-contradiction, both pictures cannot be true at the same time. Mankind had only one origin and has had only one history. Thus only one picture can be true.

In this section we shall examine evidence and match it with the two opposing paradigms, Naturalism, and Creationism. We will start by analyzing Naturalism. We will see that the naturalistic belief system for man's origin does not fit with reality.

Evolutionism summary

Let us review evolutionism's picture for man's origin. According to this view, life including man is the product of a long series of naturalistic (evolutionary) changes over millions and millions of years of time.

According to the evolutionary belief system, life gradually changed from simple to more complex forms over vast time. Atheistic evolutionists claim that the upward climb of life just happened by pure mindless chance. According to them, if the whole process were to start all over again, a completely different outcome probably would result. Because it all happened by chance, outcome cannot be pre-determined.

Of course a Christian cannot hold an atheistic world view. However, surprising as it may seem, many Christian college and seminary professors are ardent supporters of Darwinism and energetically fight against Biblical creationism. How then does a Christian professor embrace Darwinism? He does it by attempting to compromise the two opposing views of theism vs. Naturalism. Some refer to this compromise as theistic evolutionism.

Theistic evolutionists believe that a supreme being could have been involved in some way or another at some point or points in the otherwise purely random naturalistic process. Atheism of course is unacceptable to a Christian. The Christian world-view is theistic. However, because of the powerful indoctrination students receive from the educational establishments, including graduate schools, many come away believing that evolutionism is true and hence unbeatable. They also believe that evolutionism is religiously neutral. But neither of these beliefs is correct.

Phillip Johnson (mentioned in the previous chapter) has provided a detailed analysis of this compromise. He terms it "theistic naturalism"[116] and shows how it is logically contradictory and out of touch with reality.

> If theologians hope to win a place in reality, however, they have to stop seeking the approval of naturalists and advance their own theory of knowledge. ... The opposition between the biblical and naturalistic stories is fundamental, and neither side can compromise over

---

[116]Johnson, *Reason*, p. 97

it. To compromise is to surrender. ... The difference between the two ways of thinking is fundamental, and theists who try to bridge it by a superficial compromise end up by tacitly accepting naturalism.[117]

He continues with his perceptive analysis of this situation.

> What theistic evolutionists have failed above all to comprehend is that the conflict is not over 'facts' but over ways of thinking. The problem is not just with any specific doctrine of Darwinian science, but with the naturalistic rules of thought that Darwinian scientists employ to derive those doctrines. ... The specific answers they [theistic evolutionists] derive may or may not be reconcilable with theism, but the manner of thinking is profoundly atheistic. To accept the answers as indubitably true is inevitably to accept the thinking that generated those answers. That is why I think the appropriate term for the accommodationist position is not 'theistic evolution,' but rather *theistic naturalism*. Under either name, it is a disastrous error.[118]

My experience with theistic evolutionists has shown that they do not derive their belief about man's origin from Scripture. Instead they take the teachings of naturalism concerning man's origin as their absolute standard for truth in this area. They then try one scheme or another to try to force Scripture to fit with evolutionism. Evolutionists, theistic or otherwise, claim that the fossil

---

[117]Johnson, *Reason*, pp. 107-109

[118]Phillip E. Johnson, "Shouting 'Heresy' in the Temple of Darwin" *Christianity Today* October 24, 1994, p. 26

evidence supports their belief. As we shall see, however, the actual fossil evidence does exactly the opposite. Quoting again from Phillip Johnson:

> If scientists had actually observed natural selection creating new organs, or had seen a step-by-step process of fundamental change consistently recorded in the fossil record, such observations could readily be interpreted as evidence of God's use of secondary causes to create. But Darwinian scientists have not observed anything like that. What they have done is to assume as a matter of first principle that purposeless material processes can do all the work of biological creation because, according to their philosophy, nothing else was available.[119]

A further interesting and thorough discussion illustrating the fact that the fossil record does not support evolutionism is given in the book, *Evolution: A Theory in Crisis* by Michael Denton.[120]

Dr. Denton, an Australian and a microbiologist, although not a creationist, nevertheless had the intellectual curiosity and courage to examine how well naturalism matches the real world in biology and paleontology.

> Considering that the total number of known fossil species is nearly one hundred thousand, the fact that the only relatively convincing morphological sequences are a handful of cases like the horse, which do not involve a great deal of change, and which in many cases like the elephant may not even represent phylogenetic sequences at all, serves to emphasize the

---

[119]Johnson, p. 26

[120]Michael Denton, *Evolution: A Theory in Crisis*, Bethesda MD, Adler & Adler, 1986

remarkable lack of any direct evidence for major evolutionary transformations in the fossil record.[121]

Denton claims to not believe in creation. He was simply examining the actual fossil evidence to see how well it matched with the evolutionary belief system. His conclusion is that there is no match at all.

Other evolutionary scientists have also pointed out the lack of fossil evidence. Well-known and ardent evolutionist S. J. Gould has stated:

> The extreme rarity of transitional forms in the fossil record persists as the trade secret of paleontology. The evolutionary trees that adorn our textbooks have data only at the tips and nodes of their branches; the rest is inference, however reasonable, not the evidence of fossils. ... The history of most fossil species includes two features inconsistent with gradualism: 1. *Stasis*. Most species exhibit no directional change during their tenure on earth. They appear in the fossil record looking much the same as when they disappear; morphological change is usually limited and directionless. 2. *Sudden Appearance*. In any local area, a species does not arise gradually by the steady trans- formation of its ancestors; it appears all at once and 'fully formed.'[122]

Again Gould states,

> The three-leveled, five-kingdom system may appear, at first glance, to record an inevitable progress in the history of life that I have often opposed in these

---

[121]Michael Denton, *Evolution: A Theory in Crisis*, p. 185

[122]S. J. Gould, "Evolution's Erratic Pace" *Natural History*, Vol. 86, No. 5, p. 14 (May, 1977).

columns. Increasing diversity and multiple transitions seem to reflect a determined and inexorable progression toward higher things. But the paleontological record supports no such interpretation. There has been no steady progress in the higher development of organic design. We have had, instead, vast stretches of little or no change and one evolutionary burst that created the whole system.[123]

In his well-known book, *Darwin on Trial*, Phillip Johnson, a law professor at University of California, Berkeley, and a specialist in evidence and logic, comments:

The fossil record was revisited in the 1970s in works by Stephen Jay Gould, Niles Eldredge, and Steven Stanley. Gould and Eldredge proposed a new theory they called 'punctuated equilibrium' ('punk eek' to the irreverent), to deal with an embarrassing fact: the fossil record today on the whole looks very much as it did in 1859, despite the fact that an enormous amount of fossil hunting has gone on in the intervening years. ... In short, if evolution means the gradual change of one kind of organism into another kind, the outstanding characteristic of the fossil record is the absence of evidence for evolution.[124]

Fossil evidence provides no support for the idea that one type of animal has changed into another type of animal. For example, fish appear suddenly in the fossil record as fish. No evidence has been found of their

---

[123]S. J. Gould, "The Five Kingdoms" *Natural History*, Vol. 85, No. 6, p. 37 (June-July, 1976).

[124]Phillip Johnson, *Darwin on Trial*, Downers Grove IL, InterVarsity Press, 1991, p. 50

becoming or developing into fish from something else. Fish suddenly appear in the record as fish; they remained as fish; they are still fish. How do we recognize a fish in the fossil record? We recognize a fish in the fossil record because it looks like present-day fish. Quoting again Johnson's statement, "In short, if evolution means the gradual change of one kind of organism into another kind, the outstanding characteristic of the fossil record is the absence of evidence for evolution."[125]

Fossils and man

Now let's look specifically at some fossil evidence relating to the origin of man, since that is our topic.

> Shock waves are reverberating through the halls of evolution at the recent redating of the Java Solo (Ngandong Beds) *Homo erectus* fossil skulls. These alleged evolutionary ancestors of modern humans were assumed to be old. The new data — a maximum of 46,000 years before the present (YBP) with a probable date of 27,000 YBP — strongly suggests that *Homo erectus* coexisted with anatomically modern humans (*Homo sapiens*) long after *Homo erectus* was supposed to have become extinct. These finds conflict with the concept of human evolution. The discovery was reported in *Science*, 13 December 1996, by a team headed by Carl Swisher III and G. H. Curtis of the Berkeley Geochronology Center.[126]

Another instance is reported in *National Geographic*,

---

[125]Johnson, *Darwin on Trial*, p. 50

[126] Marvin Lubenow, "Alleged Evolutionary Ancestors Coexisted With Modern Humans" *Acts & Facts*, April, 1997, p. i.

where a diagram shows the location where various fossils, including *Zinjanthropus*, were found.[127] *Zinjanthropus* is supposedly a link between animal and man. Also listed on the diagram however is *Homo Habilis*, a form considered more modern by evolutionists, and it was found <u>lower</u> in the strata. This is exactly opposite from what the evolution picture would expect.

The dating of skull 1470 (Kenya Museum number) found by Richard Leakey, the son of Louis Leakey caused quite a stir in anthropological circles. The dating of 1470 at 2.8 million years not only wrecked the proposed ancestral status of africanus, but, as Leakey indicated, seriously upset the rest of evolutionary theory applied to man. The reason this fossil was so upsetting was because by the evolutionists' own dating methods, it was one of the oldest "human" fossils known. It was older than *Zinjanthropus*, older than Cro-Magnon, older than Neanderthal, and yet, compared with "newer" fossils, Skull 1470 looked more human. This again was exactly opposite from what evolutionism would expect.

Still more recently, a scientist, after examining over 2,000 skulls concluded that Neanderthal was not primitive man. Instead, Neanderthal was in fact ancestor of modern-day Europeans: Germans, Scandinavians, Dutch, etc. Neanderthal has been popularized and is commonly referred to as cave man. "But the fact is, the West European Neanderthals are today's West Europeans."[128] Numerous other examples could be cited.

---

[127] Melvin M. Payne, Sc.D. (Illustrations by Joseph J. Scherschel), "Preserving the Treasures of Olduvai Gorge" *National Geographic*, Vol. 130, #5, November 1966, p. 707.

[128] John Holmes, "Neanderthals Linked to West Europeans" *Insight*, September 11, 1989, p. 56

Many anthropologists today consider Neanderthal as conspecific with modern man — that is as simply a variety or race of modern man. This is reflected in the technical terminology now often used: He used to be called Homo neanderthalensis; now he is called Homo sapiens neanderthalensis, meaning the Neanderthal type of modern man.

"The dating of this 'last' Neanderthal suggests that Neanderthals could not possibly be ancestors of modern Europeans"[129] "Everyone agrees on one thing: if the new dating methods are accurate, then the Neanderthals, long overlapped with modern humans, clearly can't be regarded simply as more-primitive versions of ourselves."[130]

A further article summarizing the dilemma faced by the evolutionary paradigm when forced to consider actual fossil evidence appeared in *U.S. News & World Report*. Although the article didn't consider creation, it explained that all previous evolutionary ideas up until the present of where and how man originated have now been shown to be wrong.

> 'The fossil record contains a wealth of information about these hominids that we have only begun to decode,' says Robert Blumenschine, a paleoanthropologist at Rutgers University. 'The real question is whether we have enough imagination to reconstruct their lives.'[131]

---

[129]William F. Allman, "Who We Were: The Origins of Modern Humans" *U.S. News & World Report*, September 16, 1991, p. 55

[130]James Shreeve, "The deepening conundrum of Neanderthal Man" *Smithsonian*, December 1991, p. 120.

[131]William Allman, "The First Humans" *U.S. News & World Report*, February 27, 1989, p. 56

A fairly thorough analysis of fossil evidence relating to man's origin was also carried out by William Fix. Although Fix emphasizes that he does not classify himself as a creationist, he nevertheless states,

> Regardless of how robustly dogmatic assertions to the contrary may be, even if they are made by the American Association for the Advancement of Science and endorsed by fifty thousand scientists, human evolution is simply not proven.[132]

After thoroughly examining available evidence, William Fix was led to conclude that paleontological evidence does not at all support a naturalistic explanation for the origin of man. Many other examples of statements similar to those listed above can be found in the scientific literature. Fossil evidence simply does not support the idea that man has evolved upward from the animal. Evolutionism does not agree with fossil reality.

In summary we conclude that the available fossil evidence just does not fit with man originating through an evolutionary process upward from the animals. Although fossil evidence does not support an evolutionary origin for man, what about evidence from another area of science, the science of genetics? We shall consider that next.

DNA evidence

In addition to negative fossil evidence for a naturalistic explanation of man's origin, biochemical evidence must also be considered. For example, through studying

---

[132]William Fix, *The Bone Peddlers*, New York, Macmillan, 1984, p. 151

mitochondrial DNA it is possible to trace one's ancestry. Recent studies of mitochondrial DNA led to a very important discovery. When reporting this important discovery, the widely-read magazine, *Newsweek* displayed on its cover a colorful sketch of Adam and Eve supposedly representing the Biblical account of the first humans, along with the headline in large letters, "The Search For Adam and Eve."[133] Inside, the article explained that scientists studying mitochondrial DNA had made a very significant discovery.

The actual scientific evidence indicated that all human beings alive on earth today appear to be descended from one original woman. The news item in *Newsweek* stated, "Trained in molecular biology, they [scientists] looked at an international assortment of genes and picked up a trail of DNA that led them to a single woman from whom we are all descended."[134](brackets mine)

It is also interesting to observe how in that article the world-view of naturalism was superimposed on the evidence. Biblical creation as an explanation was specifically ruled out, even though it fit nicely with the actual evidence. Again quoting from the article,

> All the babies' DNA could be traced back, ultimately, to one woman. In itself that wasn't surprising, at least not to statisticians familiar with the quirks of genetic inheritance. 'There *must* be one lucky mother,' Wilson says. 'I worry about the term "Eve" a little bit because of the implication that in

---

[133]John Tierney, Lynda Wright, & Karen Springen, "The Search For Adam and Eve" *Newsweek*, January 11, 1988, pp. 46-52

[134]Tierney, Wright, & Springen, p. 46

her generation there were only two people. We are not saying that. We're saying that in her generation there was some unknown number of men and women, probably a fairly large number, maybe a few thousand.'[135] (emphasis his)

According to the Bible, Adam and Eve were the first two people from whom all on earth today are descended. Even though the Biblical account is consistent with the scientific evidence, it appears as though a conscious effort was made to rule it out from consideration. It is interesting to note, however, that even those with a naturalistic world-view cannot resist using Biblical terminology in their title, "The Search for Adam and Eve."

The discovery that all human beings descended from one original woman seemed to be quite surprising to evolutionists. Their expectation was that man had probably arisen at several different locations on earth. Hence they were faced with the question of why the evidence all points back to <u>one</u> original woman. While that might be a puzzle for the evolutionary explanation for origins, it is not at all surprising from the Biblical perspective. Genesis 3:20 - "And Adam called his wife's name Eve; because she was the mother of all living." From the Biblical perspective, Adam and Eve were indeed the first two people. All human beings alive on earth today <u>are</u> descended from them. This modern evidence fits nicely with the creation view.

After the *Newsweek* article appeared, the discussion about the evidence shown by mitochondrial DNA has

---

[135] Tierney, Wright, & Springen, p. 50

continued and also has been updated.[136] Some investigators have challenged the notion that the original woman was from Africa. They suggest instead that "Eve" may have been from Asia or the Middle East. While the location may be debated, the fact of one original woman apparently is not.[137]

A natural question is why mitochondrial DNA was used to trace female ancestry rather than ancestry for both genders. The reason is: "The molecule has a further characteristic—it is inherited only from the mother. Hence, it provides a pedigree. Each individual is connected by an unbroken chain of mothers back into the past."[138] Mitochondrial DNA comes from outside the nucleus of a cell. It is not a mixture of genes from both parents as is nuclear DNA, so it preserves a family record that isn't scrambled every generation.

Attempts to construct a family line for human males have in the past been hindered because of the mixing of both parents' genes in the nucleus of the cell. Now however, that hindrance seems to have been overcome. Scientists have carefully studied a section of the Y chromosome passed only through the male line.

> Scientists think they have found strong evidence of an ancestral 'Adam' about 188,000 years ago to go with the previously discovered 'Eve.' The

---

[136]Greg J. Beasley, "Is the African 'Eve' Misconceived?" *Creation Ex Nihilo Technical Journal*, Vol. 6 (1), 1992, pp. 42-48

[137]Ann Gibbons, "Mitochondrial Eve: Wounded, But Not Dead Yet" *Science* 14 August 1992, pp. 873-875

[138]James Krieger, "Evidence accrues for specific female ancestor" *Chemical & Engineering News*, February 6, 1989, p. 28

scientists used certain male-specific segments of the Y chromosome, the chromosome passed from father to son, to trace the common ancestor of every man now on Earth to that period.[139]

Biochemical evidence from DNA studies supports the idea that all people on earth originated from one man and one woman.

After tracing man's origin back to one man and one woman, an important question raises itself. How long ago did the first woman live on earth? What is the time frame involved? In the article appearing in Newsweek in 1988[140] a date of 200,000 years was given. According to the evolutionism view, humans were believed to have existed for a million years or more. Therefore, it was quite shocking to obtain a date of only about 200,000 years.

> What shocked them about Mitochondrial Mom was her birthday, which the Berkeley researchers calculated by counting the mutations that have occurred to her DNA.[141]

How was this date of 200,000 years obtained? Over time, mutations occur in the DNA of humans (and other animals). How many mutations have occurred since Eve? How fast do mutations occur? In other words, what is the rate at which the mitochondrial DNA clock runs? If

---

[139]John Noble Wilford, "Researchers dig up evidence of 'Adam,' father of all men" *The Oregonian*, November 23, 1995, p. A13. See also Michael F. Hammer, "A recent common ancestry for human Y chromosomes," *Nature*, November 23, 1995 (vol. 378, issue 6555) p. 376-8.

[140] Tierney, Wright, & Springen

[141] Tierney, Wright, & Springen, p. 50

the number of mutations since Eve were known, and if the mutation rate were also known, then one could calculate how long ago mitochondrial Eve lived.

Because of their evolutionist world-view, and their belief that humans had been here for a million years or more, those who investigated the mitochondrial DNA attempted to calibrate the clock in accord with their belief system. Only by speculating or hypothesizing about the past could a clock rate be obtained because no actual rates for the mitochondrial clock had been observed. Using evolutionary speculation,

> They looked at the most distant branches of the family tree—the DNA types most different from one another—and worked backward to figure out how many steps it would have taken for Eve's original DNA to mutate into these different types. They assumed that these mutations occurred at a regular rate—a controversial assumption that might be wrong...[142]

What was the result of this speculative calculation? "By this molecular calculus, Eve must have lived about 200,000 years ago (the range is between 140,000 and 290,000 years)."[143]

Thus even by using their very slow-gradual-change idea of evolutionism, their theoretical clock rate yielded a date for the first Eve that was uncomfortably less than a million years or more. But as already mentioned above, further research using the Y chromosome and male ancestry, brought the first man Adam also much closer in

---

[142] Tierney, Wright, & Springen, p. 50

[143] Tierney, Wright, & Springen, p. 50

time than the million or more years of evolutionist belief.

What has been the result of further investigation since the 1988 and 1995 results were published? An interesting subsequent development has been calibration of the mitochondrial DNA clock by using actually observed data rather than by using speculations from evolutionism. The result has shown that the clock ticks very much faster than expected.

> Mitochondrial DNA appears to mutate much faster than expected, prompting new DNA forensics procedures and raising troubling questions about the dating of evolutionary events. In 1991, Russians exhumed a Siberian grave containing nine skeletons thought to be the remains of the last Russian tsar, Nicholas II, and his family and retinue, who were shot by firing squad in 1918. But two bodies were missing, so no one could be absolutely certain of the identity of the remains. And DNA testing done in 1992—expected to settle the issue quickly—instead raised a new mystery.[144]

The mystery concerned dates relating to the clock rate. It appears that mutations occur at a much more rapid rate than had been imagined. Although there seems to be considerable debate about the cause of the faster rate, the faster rate has been verified by independent investigations.

> Regardless of the cause, evolutionists are most concerned about the effect of a faster mutation rate. For example, researchers have calculated that "mitochon-

drial Eve"— the woman whose mtDNA was ancestral to that in all living people— lived 100,000 to 200,000 years ago in Africa. Using the new clock, she would be a mere 6000 years old.[145]

The 6000 year date for Eve brings to mind the Biblical time scale and is an uncomfortable result for evolutionism. In a summary of the situation, Ann Gibbons, author of the *Science* article makes a most interesting comment followed by a most profound question. She writes, "No one thinks that's the case [that Eve is 6000 years old], but at what point should models switch from one mtDNA time zone to the other?"[146]

That is a very perceptive question. As David Buckna commented, "Perhaps Ann Gibbons should have written, 'No <u>evolutionist</u> thinks that's the case...'"[147]

Such evidence is in agreement with creation as the origin of mankind. However, evolutionists have postulated an escape hatch to get around this evidence. They postulate that mankind actually did originate from several different individuals in agreement with evolutionary theory. Then to explain the negative evidence for these different individuals, they postulate that the genetic lines of these other individuals was subsequently lost when all of the individuals in those lines died out and each of the other lines became extinct without leaving any evidence.

Rather than generating so many ad hoc assumptions to explain away negative evidence, how much better it

---

[145] Gibbons, p. 29.

[146] Gibbons, p. 29

[147] David Buckna, personal communication

would be to straight-forwardly accept what the Creator has told us. His Word is true.

In summary, the actual evidence available from both fossils and modern biochemistry match with the Biblical account of creation.

SELECTED BIBLIOGRAPHY

Allman, William, "The First Humans" *U.S. News & World Report*, February 27, 1989, p. 56

Allman, William F. with Joannie M. Schrof, "Lost Empires of the Americas" *U.S. News & World Report*, April 2, 1990, p. 46

Allman, William F., "Who We Were: The Origins of Modern Humans" *U.S. News & World Report*, September 16, 1991, p. 55

Bayard, D. T., "Early Thai Bronze: Analysis and New Dates" *Science*, 30 June 1972, p. 1412.

Beasley, Greg J., "Is the African 'Eve' Misconceived?" *Creation Ex Nihilo Technical Journal*, Vol. 6 (1), 1992, pp. 42-48

Berlitz, Charles, *Mysteries From Forgotten Worlds*, Garden City NY, Doubleday & Co., 1972

Boland, Charles Michael, *They all discovered America*, New York, Permabook, 1963;

Bower, Bruce, "Rational Mind Designs: Research into the ecology of thought treads on contested terrain" *Science News*, July 13, 1996, pp. 24-25

Branda, Richard F., and John W. Eaton, "Skin Color and Nutrient Photolysis: An Evolutionary Hypothesis," *Science*, 18 August 1978, p. 625.

Chichen Itza, Ediciones Alducin, Mexico, 1984, pp. 45-46

Clarke, Urana, "How Our Music Began" *The Book of Knowledge* (Volume 18) New York, 1957

Cooper, Bill, *After The Flood: The Early Post-Flood History of Europe*, New Wine Press, West Sussex, England, 1995

Corliss, William R., *Ancient Man: A Handbook of Puzzling Artifacts*, Glen Arm MD, The Sourcebook Project, 1978

Cremo, Michael A. and Richard L. Thompson, *Forbidden Archeology*, San Diego, Govardhan Hill Publishing, 1993

Davidovits, Dr. Joseph, and Margie Morris, *The Pyramids: An Enigma Solved*, New York, Dorset Press, 1990

"Debate at East Tennessee State University" *Acts & Facts*, July 1996, p. 2

Denton, Michael, Evo*lution: A Theory in Crisis*, Bethesda MD, Adler & Adler, 1986

Fell, Barry, America B.C.: *Ancient Settlers in the New World*, New York, Quadrangle/The New York Times Book Co., 1977 (also by Barry Fell, *Bronze Age America*);

Fix, William, *The Bone Peddlers*, New York, Macmillan, 1984

Gamkrelidze, Thomas V., and V. V. Ivanov, "The Early History of Indo-European Languages" *Scientific American*, March 1990, p. 110.

Gibbons, Ann, "Mitochondrial Eve: Wounded, But Not Dead Yet" *Science* 14 August 1992, pp. 873-875

————————"Calibrating the Mitochondrial Clock" *Science*, 2 January 1998 (volume 279, number 5347), p. 28

Gould, S. J., "Evolution's Erratic Pace" *Natural History*, Vol. 86, No. 5, p. 14 (May, 1977).

———————— "The Five Kingdoms" *Natural History*, Vol. 85, No. 6, p. 37 (June-July, 1976).

Gwynne, Peter, "Earth's seismicity destroyed Chimu irrigation system" *Industrial Research & Development*, September 1982, p. 59.

Ham, Ken, Andrew Snelling, and Carl Wieland, *The Answers Book*, Green Forest, AR: Master Books, 1990

Hammer, Michael F., "A recent common ancestry for human Y chromosomes, *Nature*, November 23, 1995 (vol. 378, issue 6555) p. 376-8.

Hancock, Graham, *Fingerprints of the Gods*, New York, Crown Trade Paperbacks, 1995;

Hapgood, Charles, *Maps of the Ancient Sea Kings: Evidence of Advanced Civilization in the Ice Age*, Philadelphia, Chilton Books, 1966

Heyerdahl, Thor, *Aku Aku: the secret of Easter Island*, Chicago: Rand McNally, 1958

——— *Kon Tiki: across the Pacific by raft*, Chicago: Rand McNally, 1950.

Heyerdahl, Thor, and Arne Skj^lsvold, "Archaeological Evidence of Pre-Spanish Visits to the Galapagos Islands," *Mem. No. 12, Society for American Archaeology* 1956

Hislop, Rev. Alexander, *The Two Babylons*, Neptune NJ, Loizeaux Brothers, 1959

Holmes, John, "Neanderthals Linked to West Europeans" *Insight,* September 11, 1989, p. 56

Homer, *The Odyssey*, Book 19 (The Harvard Classics, edited by Charles W. Eliot LL.D., Translated by S.H. Butcher & A. Lang,) P.F. Collier & Son New York (1909).

Johnson, Phillip E., *Darwin On Trial*, Downers Grove IL, InterVarsity Press, 1993

——— "Shouting 'Heresy' in the Temple of Darwin" *Christianity Today* October 24, 1994, p. 26.

———*Reason in the Balance*, Downers Grove IL, InterVarsity Press, 1995

———"Putting Reason in the Balance: An Interview with Phillip E. Johnson" *Bible-Science News*, September 1995, p. 2.

Johnston, Thomas Crawford, *Did the Phoenicians discover America?* Houston, St. Thomas Press, 1965

Keyser, Paul T., "The Purpose of the Parthian Galvanic Cells: A First-Century A.D. Electric Battery Used for Analgesia" *Journal of Near Eastern Studies*, 52 no. 2 (1993), p. 98.

Krieger, James, "Evidence accrues for specific female ancestor" *Chemical & Engineering News*, February 6, 1989, p. 28

Las lineas Nazca, Lima, Perú, LibrerÌas ABC S.A., 1978

Lubenow, Marvin, "Alleged Evolutionary Ancestors Coexisted With Modern Humans" *Acts & Facts*, April, 1997

Mendelssohn, Kurt, "A Scientist Looks at the Pyramids" *American Scientist*, 1971 March-April, p. 210.

Moore, Thomas, "Thor Heyerdahl: Sail*ing Against the Current*" U.S. News & World Report, April 2, 1990, p. 60

Morley, Silvanus, *The Ancient Maya*, Stanford University Press, 1956

Morris, Henry, *The Long War Against God: The History and Impact of the Creation/Evolution Conflict*, Grand Rapids, Baker Book House, 1989

————*The Defender's Study Bible*, Grand Rapids, World Publishing, 1995

"Neandertal noisemaker" *Science News*, November 23, 1996, p. 328

Neugebauer, O., *The Exact Sciences in Antiquity*, New York, Dover Publications, 1969;

Noebel, David A., *Understanding the Times*, Summit Press, Manitou Springs, CO, 1991

Noorbergen, Rene, *Secrets of the Lost Races: New Discoveries of Advanced Technology in Ancient Civilizations*, Collegedale TN, Norcom Publishing Corp., 1992

Oard, Michael J., *An Ice Age Caused by the Genesis Flood*, San Diego, Institute for Creation Research, 1990

"The Oldest Mine?" *Time*, January 13, 1975, p. 65.

Patton, Robert, "OOPARTS" *Omni*, September 1982, p. 54.

Payne, Melvin M., Sc.D. (Illustrations by Joseph J. Scherschel), "Preserving the Treasures of Olduvai Gorge" *National Geographic*, Vol. 130, #5, November 1966, p. 707.

Schaeffer, Francis, *The God Who Is There: Speaking historic Christianity into the twentieth century*, Chicago, InterVarsity Press, 1968

"The Seminal Science" *Mosaic* May/June 1978, pp. 2-8

Shreeve, James, "The deepening conundrum of Neanderthal Man" *Smithsonian*, December 1991, p. 120.

Steiger, Brad, "Were Ancient Scientists Really Tuned to Today?" *Parade*, March 4, 1979, p. 10

Tierney, John, Lynda Wright, & Karen Springen, "The Search For Adam and Eve" *Newsweek*, January 11, 1988, pp. 46-52

Von Däniken, Erich, *Chariots of the Gods?: Unsolved Mysteries of the Past*, New York, G. P. Putnam's Sons, 1969 (translated by Michael Heron).

Wade, Nicholas, "Thomas S. Kuhn: Revolutionary Theorist of Science," *Science*, 8 July 1977, p. 144.

Wilford, John Noble, "Researchers dig up evidence of 'Adam,' father of all men" *The Oregonian*, November 23, 1995, p. A13.

Woodman, Jim, *Nazca: Journey to the Sun*, New York, Pocket Books (Simon & Schuster), pp. 50-55

INDEX